BRITAIN'S

Edward F. Hart

True Crime Library — No. 5
A Forum Press Book
by the Paperback Division of
Forum Design,
P.O. Box 158, London SE 20 7QA.

An Imprint of True Crime Library
© 1993 by Edward T. Hart
All rights reserved

Typeset by Techniset,
1 Back Cross Lane, Newton-le-Willows, Merseyside WA12 9YE.
Printed and bound in Great Britain by
Harper Collins Manufacturing, Glasgow.

ISBN 1 874358 03 6

Edward Hart operated as a crime correspondent in Fleet Street during the fifties and sixties ... and later freelanced for newspapers and magazines on both sides of the Atlantic.

He worked closely with two of Scotland Yard's most legendary commanders ...

Jack Capstick, founder of the Ghost Squad who was dubbed 'Charlie Artful' by the underworld; and Bert Wickstead, the tough East End copper known as 'The Gangbuster' who led the Serious Crime Squad during its heyday.

He has also written over twenty books, mostly ghosted autobiographies.

For
Charlie Artful
and the
Cobblestone Fighter

CONTENTS

Our acknowledgements to David Withey, local history librarian at the London Borough of Islington Libraries Department for the photographs of Darby Sabini, The Saffron Hill gang, the Catholic Parade and Pasquala Poppa. Our thanks also to Camden Local Studies Library for the photograph of the Griffin.

Foreword

It was the summer of 1956, and Billy Hill had just announced to an Old Bailey jury, "I am king of the underworld."

I asked Jack Capstick, Scotland Yard's legendary commander — known as 'Charlie Artful' — just how he rated the flamboyant Billy in the all-time league of gang leaders. "Second only to Darby Sabini," he replied.

Now this surprised me. For although I was working as a crime correspondent in Fleet Street, I knew very little about Sabini. I had heard journalists who remembered the Twenties and the Thirties describe him somewhat disparagingly as a "racecourse thug"; and I'd also been told that he had been regarded as a demi-hero by his fellow inhabitants in the slumland of London's Little Italy, the name by which pre-war Clerkenwell was known. But I hadn't looked upon him as a major figure in the sphere of organised crime.

"Was Sabini really that big?" I asked.

Capstick, who loved to reminisce, puffed contentedly at his pipe before answering. "Put it this way," he said. "Compared to Darby Sabini, all the other British gang leaders down the years have been merely messenger boys. The majority of them have been mindless thugs who understood only how to terrorise. Some had enough imagination to plan major robberies. But Darby had it all.

"He had the charisma needed to build a huge gangster army. He was strong enough to control these men of violence without ever needing to raise his voice. And above all else, he was intelligent enough to out-think and out-manoeuvre his enemies over and over again. He could barely read or write, and yet he possessed a tactical genius such as few army commanders will ever know. He set out with the intention of protecting his people. He ended up by creating a criminal empire the like of which Britain had never seen before ... and will almost certainly never see again."

There was grudging admiration in Capstick's voice, and this seemed strange coming from such a man. For this was no ordinary copper. The phrase 'a legend in his own lifetime' is apt to be over-used; but in Jack Capstick's case, it was the right one. After pounding the beat, he had risen through the ranks to reach the heights, a rare thing in that day and age.

He had led both the Murder Squad and the Flying Squad. He had founded the Ghost Squad, the élite under-cover force which infiltrated organised crime. And he was the policeman major criminals feared above all others. Hunting down the top villains had become his way of life. So could he really find it possible to admire a gangster such as Darby Sabini?

He shrugged. "Maybe respect is a better word," he said. "Darby had a certain integrity you don't find very often with villains. He had his own code of honour and he abided by it. His word was his bond.

"He was a criminal, because he broke the law. But he always looked upon violence as a last resort, and in his case it was never mindless violence. He claimed that no honest man ever had anything to fear from him ... and this was true. He wasn't a trickster, a mugger or a thief. His battles were always waged against other gangs. In his own way, he was a very moral man. He would never allow his followers to use bad language in front of a woman. He was a devout Catholic, and St. Peter's in Clerkenwell was largely rebuilt with his money."

He paused and smiled. "Maybe you ought to write a book about him. It's time somebody did."

That was the day when the seeds for this book were sown. However, I soon discovered that this would be no easy task. A visit to the library of the *Daily Mail* — then my current paper — produced only a handful of cuttings, and for this there was a good reason. During his heyday Sabini never saw the inside of a jail. So any newspaper that so much as hinted that he might have criminal connections would receive a writ almost before the ink had time to dry. Invariably they settled out of court. The process eventually became so expensive that copy tasters were given instructions to spike any story carrying his name.

So with little choice in the matter, I set off down strange paths that led me into the world of Darby Sabini ... a world of club-owners and bouncers, boxers and jockeys, book-makers and their bruisers, robbers and racketeers. Most of them had their own stories to tell, and none more interesting than those of the jockeys, Jack Leach and Harry Carr. Darby had a very special affection for jockeys.

Jack Leach recalled the day he'd lost on a favourite at Longchamp, never a wise thing to do. Racegoers had thrown gravel at him as he'd come riding in, and a hard core of trouble-makers lay in wait as he left the jockeys' room. But before the mob could reach him, he was surrounded by Sabini soldiers, big men with faces so hard and forbidding that the mob rapidly lost its taste for blood. With that human shield around him, Leach left Longchamp and was delivered safely to his Paris hotel. Still a little mystified, Leach tried to thank his saviours. At this, their leader shrugged casually. "Darby told us to look after you," he said.

The Queen's jockey, Harry Carr, recounted a story from his apprentice days. He was en route to the Brighton racecourse with another young jockey. At Victoria, they stepped into a carriage filled with Sabini's followers and rashly allowed themselves to be inveigled into a game of cards. In no time at all they had lost all their money, a fiver apiece, no mean sum in those days.

Some five minutes later, the carriage door slid open and Darby entered, realising instantly what had happened.

"How much money have you lost?" he asked the young jockeys.

"A fiver," they replied in unison.

He turned to his soldiers. "Give them their fivers back," he said quietly. The fivers were returned.

"Now give them another fiver," he said.

At this there was some shuffling in the ranks, but no one dared disobey. He then escorted the apprentices to an empty carriage and lectured them like a Dutch uncle. He ended the soliloquy by telling them firmly, "Remember, never ever gamble with villains."

Further down the trail, I encountered Johnny Cattini, a mildly spoken man who told me with a trace of pride how he must have left his trademark on at least a hundred men: a V-shaped scar running from ear to chin.

"Forehand and backhand," he said. "All over before they had time to blink. They never felt a thing until the stitching began."

Then there was the jovial Joe Pegg, known to his numerous friends as 'The Captain'. He had enjoyed going into the Griffin on a Saturday night and watching Darby, gold teeth glinting in the bar lights, as he sang his favourite song 'Rosie Magoola'.

"He had a beautiful voice, a true Italian tenor," explained Joe. "If he'd had it trained, he could have made a fortune; but then money meant nothing at all to Darby. He was a man totally devoid of ambition. As long as he had a roof over his head, enough food to see him through the week and ten bob in his pocket to buy him a drink, he was happy."

But for me the big breakthrough came when I first met Georgie Sewell, Darby's lieutenant and right hand man ... as remarkable a character in his own right as Darby himself.

He was known as 'The Cobblestone Fighter' and was said to be invincible in this raw-knuckle brand of battling. He never carried a weapon, unless his fists could be so described. Yet he was the most feared of all the Sabini soldiers. Rival gangs had more than once set up ambushes and slashed his face to ribbons with their cut-throats, the favoured weapon of the day. But on each occasion, before the wounds had even healed, he would hunt down his assailants one by one and his vengeance would be awesome. Unless you cared to murder him — and the gallows put a curb on such ambitions — there was no way of stopping such a man.

By the time I came to know him he had long since retired from the criminal ranks and mellowed into an equable old man. A born raconteur. He ran the most trouble-free club in Soho, yet every now and then when someone stepped out of line, that scarred face would become hard again and you could sense the menace that had gone before. But there was kindness too, and essentially he was a good man, a good husband, a good father and a good friend to me. In recalling the life and times of Darby Sabini we spent countless hours over toast, Genoa cake and endless cups of tea, often talking well into the early hours. He introduced me to old comrades, the remnants of the most formidable gangland army Britain has ever known.

As a crime correspondent, I was aware of my good fortune, for I was being given a passport into a section of the underworld where hitherto the frontier had always been closed.

He had described Darby Sabini to me as "a prince of a fellow, a man in a class of his own." Then he'd paused and said, "Someone should write a book about him." I had heard that somewhere before.

It has been a long journey, but here for Charlie Artful and the Cobblestone Fighter, and for you, is that book at last.

1

A RELUCTANT KINGSHIP

"Who needs a bruised face on a Sunday morning?" — Darby Sabini, attempting to reason with the Elephant gang enforcer Monkey Benneyworth.

It was raining in Little Italy. Pavements glittered wetly under the lamplights, and derelicts huddled in every doorway, watching the night go by.

Darby Sabini, wrapped in some strange private world of his own, walked in the open seemingly unaware of the wind and the rain. The collar of his dark jacket was upturned. His check-cap tilted over his right ear and a cigarette dangled from the corner of his mouth. He was a powerful man with wide shoulders tapering down to bullfighter hips. To the denizens of this square mile of London, huddled on a hillside under the shadow of St Paul's, he had always been something special. According to legend, he was a direct descendant of the Sabines; and, in this band of exiles, that gave him a kind of kingship.

The Italians, the most persecuted race in the city, looked upon him as their protector, a saviour to lead them to better days. Mind you, there was little about the man to suggest such a thing. He lived in a hovel on Saffron Hill and wore the clothes of a peasant. Any self-appointed shrink would have taken one look at Darby and known instantly that he would never amount to much. He was too indolent, too short of ambition, to ever be a hero.

The whalebone of pride which stiffens the back of a true man appeared to be totally missing from this burly fellow.

Admittedly he had certain talents. As a professional fighter, he had strung up a long unbeaten run. While still in his teens, he scored a first-round knock-out of Fred Sutton, until then the rising star of the middleweight division. There had even been talk of a bout for the title. But champions are made by the sweat and the toil of training, and this was never Darby's way. The rest of the city would come alive with the dustcarts and the dawn. Darby would slumber on long into the morning and then rise reluctantly at noon.

Boxing promoter Dan Sullivan recognised this fatal flaw and realised that Darby could never be a contender. So instead he offered him the job of strong-arm man at the Hoxton Baths, then the roughest and most riotous fight arena in London. It was said that impromptu bouts between the paying customers were often better value than those being waged between the ropes. Darby, aided by his brothers Joe and Fred, tamed that savage place within a month ... and made the taming look easy.

But then, of course, this had been night work and Darby was one of those people who seemingly only come truly awake when the darkness wraps itself around the streets. And of all the nights of the week, Saturday night was his favourite. Now that the First World War was finally over, Little Italy had once again taken on the carnival air of its homeland.

On Saturday nights such as this, coloured lights shone out from the pubs and the clubs. Hurdy-gurdies played, and on the warm evenings there would be dancing in the streets. It was a good night on which to forget the cares of the week gone by.

As Darby reached the foot of Saffron Hill and turned left up the Clerkenwell Road, a group of Italian girls watched him go by. He barely gave them a glance. In the distance he could already see the lights of the Griffin, hear the music and the sounds spilling out. He quickened his step.

Monkey Benneyworth came into the Griffin and shook the rain from his hat. And as he did so the volume of sound around the bar ebbed for a brief second and then flowed back louder than before. He recognised the quiver for what it was. Fear! It was, after all, his stock-in-trade. Monkey Benneyworth was perhaps better known as 'the Trimmer', a tag bestowed on those who 'trimmed the sails' of other men, cutting them down to size. He was a huge man with huge hands, but it was the face of the Trimmer that told you most. There was violence, cruelty, brutality, written in every line. He was the strong-arm man for the Elephant Gang, based in the Elephant and Castle area of London south of the river. He was a man who enjoyed his work, and most of all he enjoyed his visits to Little Italy.

For hunters such as the Trimmer, this was the perfect hunting ground. In the line of business you could run the protection racket around the clubs, busting heads and breaking arms. You could beat up the men and rape the women in the certain knowledge that no one would ever complain to the police. The Italians were strangers in a strange land, preyed upon by every other race and creed. The police were their enemies too.

The Trimmer began to push his way across the crowded floor, knocking elbows, spilling drinks along the way. No one complained. The Trimmer's reputation ensured that. Upon reaching the bar, he ordered a pint of best bitter, ignoring the fact that there were others waiting too.

A barman came scurrying along, anxious to please. But at that moment the Trimmer spotted the latest addition to the Griffin, a young and nubile barmaid named Carmen Cardoza.

He surveyed the barman with scorn. He said, "I don't want you serving me, you little runt. I want her." And he threw a hand carelessly in the direction of the girl. Being new, she was probably the one person in the Griffin that night who didn't know the reputation of the Trimmer. Yet at twenty-one she was old enough to recognise the type, sense the menace of the man. And realising all this she still said, "You wait your turn, Big Man, like everybody else." Something very close to joy came into the eyes of the

Trimmer. In his sexual life, as in everything else, he was a plunderer with no great wish to take anything given freely. This was one of the reasons why the girls of Little Italy appealed to him so much. With their dark flashing eyes and proud ways, they represented a challenge. There was a spirit that needed to be broken. As befitting good Catholics, they were apt to cling to their virginity as though to a life raft.

He surveyed Carmen Cardoza with hooded, lecherous eyes. She was the type that seems to ripen in Mediterranean lands. In a few years, the hips would spread and she would become prematurely old like the matrons of her race. But for the time being she was in her prime, long-legged and with firm, full young breasts jigging delightfully beneath the red silk dress. She was voluptuous, essentially lush, very much the Trimmer's kind of woman. He promised himself that he would have her before the night was out. He knew that she wouldn't yield willingly. The thought gave him a certain pleasure.

The flickering lights of the Griffin came through the window of Silvio Massarda's flat, bathing the room in strange contrasting hues. The room was otherwise in darkness. Massarda lay upon the bed, still wearing his shirt and trousers. He was slowly undressing a blonde showgirl called Jeannie Harris.

He did so meticulously, placing each garment removed with care upon a nearby chair. It was a task which would normally have occupied his full attention. But tonight he felt oddly disenchanted with the whole affair.

He was one of those people who live their life upon a dream. In his mind's eye, he would always travel first-class, surrounded by fast exotic cars and fast exotic women. It was only occasionally on nights such as this that reality washed away the dream. The room had seen better days, and so too had Jeannie Harris. On the shadowed stages of second-rate music halls she could still conjure up a long-lost glamour. But the bright light of day betrayed her. The face was a map of battles lost and faded hopes.

Massarda tried to make-believe that he was undressing Anne Marlowe, the current star at the Lyceum, the focal point of his wildest dreams. He had never actually met her and yet he was convinced that one day they would share the good times. Mind you, he had the style and the panache to make such things come true. He had the looks of a matinee idol and flamboyant Italian ways that did his cause no harm at all. He was tall, with good shoulders and a deep chest. His dark hair was naturally waved and the whiteness of his smile was apt to have the most devastating effect upon women of all ages. The one feature that dented the image was a Roman nose. Because of this he was known in Little Italy as 'Big Shonk'. Few ever called him by any other name.

He slipped her panties down over rounded hips with practised ease . . . noticing with a touch of surprise that she really was blonde. He placed the panties upon a chair with the same care as before and then he began to caress the plump thighs with a velvet touch. Jeannie stretched out, arms and legs akimbo, like some well-fed jungle cat, and the purr was feline too. Then the hands of Massarda became still and he sighed. He had planned this as a love feast; but in his present mood, he realised it was impossible. He remembered that Darby would be in the pub across the road. He wondered whether a touch of enchantment would return after a few drinks with his friends. He slapped her carelessly along the flank.

He said, "Come on, sweetie, get dressed. The night's too young for this. Let's go out and howl. We can come back here later."

She sat up slowly as though scarcely believing what she'd heard. Then she shrugged resignedly, one more battle lost.

Massarda picked up his coat and headed for the Griffin.

As Darby pushed his way through the swing doors of the pub, the rain gusted in behind him. Immediately voices were raised in welcome and he smiled back, gold teeth glinting in the bar lights. Viewed thus he looked very Italian, dark eyes in a dark face.

The Trimmer watched him with open derision. He could never understand what these Raddies saw in this simple peasant. He thought it was maybe time he destroyed the last of their myths. He thought that maybe tonight could be the night.

Meanwhile Darby was running his eyes along the bar. He spotted the Trimmer and gave no sign that he had done so, then gave a brief nod as he sighted Georgie Sewell at the far end of the pub. Sewell nodded back without warmth and, not for the first time, Darby began to wonder about the man. Like Darby, he was a pro fighter who just might have been a champion if the desire had been a little greater. But there was a brand of violence in the soul of the man which could never be entirely slaked by gloved battles in the ring. Sewell was only a medium-sized fellow, a head shorter than the Trimmer and at least three stone lighter. Yet he could inspire more fear than anyone else Darby had ever met.

At the age of twenty-seven he was already a gangland legend and known as 'the Cobblestone Fighter'. In hand-to-hand fighting on the streets, he was considered almost unbeatable. He had made his mark as a bouncer in Soho. One night he had barred entry at a club to five members of the Rocca Family, an Italian band of enforcers based in Islington. They had told him precisely, and in graphic detail, what they intended to do to him. He had nodded matter-of-factly.

"There are five of you and so no doubt you'll carve me up," he'd said. "But take my advice. Kill me. Because if you don't, I'll hunt you down one by one if it takes me the rest of my life."

Half an hour later the police arrived to find Sewell unconscious upon the floor, his face gashed, his hands broken. Beside him lay two of his attackers equally unconscious, equally savaged. Two other members of the gang had left, supporting a battered comrade. True to his word, Sewell began hunting them down on the very next night with the stitches still holding his face together and his hands in plaster.

The trio fled the city. Their wives and families waited patiently for the return of their menfolk. When it became clear that nothing short of hell-fire would drive them back to London, the wives packed up their belongings and they too journeyed north beyond the reach of the hunter.

With such a reputation the Cobblestone Fighter would have been made welcome in any of the London gangs. He could have named his price, but that was never his way. He was a loner to be hired, but never bought. He was better at making enemies than friends. And yet in the cold heart of George Sewell, there dwelt a certain morality. Only the villains were his natural prey. Honest men had nothing at all to fear from him.

The Trimmer was making his pitch for Carmen in forthright fashion. He simply positioned himself at the centre of the bar. Even on a crowded Saturday night the other drinkers preferred to stay clear of him and queue for the two barmen flanking the girl. So with little choice in the matter, she served him.

He said, "When this place closes, you're coming with me round the clubs. So don't go making no other plans."

The sheer effrontery of his approach amused her a little. She half-smiled and said tauntingly, "I'm careful of the company I keep. When I'm desperate enough to want to go out with the likes of you, I'll let you know. Until then I suggest you stop wasting your time, and mine."

The game had almost run its course as far as the Trimmer was concerned. The smile had gone. The eyes were moody and mean.

"You guinea tarts are all the same," he told her. "You behave as though the mere idea of a man touching you would make you sick to the stomach. Then once you're stripped down for action you become sheer animals, ready to eat a fellow alive. I'm an old soldier and I know, so don't think you fool me. And don't get any bright ideas about going anywhere tonight with one of these half-baked Raddies."

He swung round to survey the room, and the Italians to a man turned away.

"If any of them so much as gives you a look, I'll tear his arm off. Tonight you're gonna make it with a real man."

Massarda and several of the Italians were looking curiously at Darby, wondering whether he would intervene. He was known to be notoriously strait-laced in matters of sex. But he was staring down into his beer and it was as though he hadn't heard a single word. Seemingly the only Italian in the bar that night with any spirit was Carmen Cardoza.

She laughed into the face of the Trimmer. "No girl in her right mind would ever go out with you and I'll tell you why. You're too old (the Trimmer was, in fact, forty-two), too ugly and too dirty."

Before she could utter another word, the big hand of the Trimmer reached out, seized the top of her dress and with one savage tug ripped it all the way down to her waist. Her full breasts sprang out and she leapt back, covering them with her hands. Her face was a mixture of outrage, astonishment and fear, with fear the predominant emotion. For the Trimmer was moving towards the bar flap intent upon finishing what he had begun.

"Now we'll see the rest of you," he said. "Take some of that sass out of you."

He put out a hand to raise the bar flap and, as if by chance, found Darby barring the way.

"Look, you've had your fun," said Darby. "Now be a reasonable man, drink up and go."

His voice was an odd blend of Southern Italy and Bow Bells; his tone quiet, almost apologetic; his whole attitude that of a man who most definitely didn't want trouble.

The Trimmer paused as a new thought came to him. Why not ruin this peasant first in front of his admirers and then go after the girl?

He looked at Darby. "No one asked you to interfere, you Raddie bastard," he said, "but now you got a choice. You either step out of my way or get flattened. My guess is that you haven't enough craw to stay there."

Georgie Sewell was watching the scene closely, although nothing showed in those cold eyes of his. The Italians were watching Darby too and scarcely believing what they saw. For his head was down as though he was incapable of meeting the Trimmer's eyes.

Darby said, "Be sensible. I've nothing against you. We're just two fellows out for a Saturday night drink and a good time. We're men of the world. We don't want to fight over a girl. Who needs a bruised face on a Sunday morning?"

He looked up at last. "I'll tell you what. Drink up and I'll buy you another. What's it going to be?"

By now the Italians were staring at him with shame, wondering how they could have been so blind for so long. But there was no mercy coming from the Trimmer, and no escape for Darby.

"I'm not drinking with a gutless coward," said the Trimmer, his words carrying clearly across the silent room. And with that, he hit Darby back-handed across the face. It was little more than a slap, and yet there was enough force in the blow to spin Darby like a top and, in reaching out to prevent himself falling, he landed face down across the bar. The Trimmer lunged forward as though about to hurl himself upon the back of Darby. But the Italians formed a thin line in front of their fallen hero.

Only Carmen could see Darby's face and what she saw brought hope to her heart. For he was smiling, a smile so cold, so chilling that he looked like a different man entirely. Yet there was no hint of this as he slowly raised himself to once again face the Trimmer. Blood was dripping from the corner of his mouth and he wiped it away with the back of his hand, considering it gravely.

He said, "If you won't drink with me and you won't reason with me, you don't give me much choice."

His tone was still that of a peace-loving man. It was only the dark eyes that said otherwise. By way of reply, the Trimmer threw a big right-hand and Darby took it on the side of the face quite deliberately as though testing it for size.

That was the last punch the Trimmer would throw that night. Darby, moving fast, caught him with a left hook to the body that drove him back against the bar and followed this up with a combination of punches to the head that brought an animal-like scream from the lips of the big man. He pitched forward unconscious, and when they turned him over there was a gasp from the onlookers.

In the space of a few brief seconds, the Trimmer had been transformed into a pathetic wreck of a man. His jaw and cheekbone had been cracked, giving the face a grotesque alignment. Blood pumped steadily from the nose and a gash over the left eye. They carried him out of the Griffin on a door and up to the tram terminus at the junction of the Clerkenwell and Grey's Inn Roads, from whence he was rushed by ambulance to the Charing Cross Hospital.

Darby watched him go, shaking his head. "You just can't reason with a fellow like that," he said.

In the early hours of Sunday morning, the men of Little Italy wended their way up Saffron Hill to the door of Darby Sabini. They came to offer allegiance to their new leader. And Darby took each hand in turn, listening to the promises and nodding in reply. His was a most reluctant kingship. Yet he was realist enough to know that it was now an inevitable, even a necessary, one.

Down in the Griffin he had committed what was in gangland terms an act of war. Once the wounds had healed the Trimmer would return. Only this time he would come mob-handed with the Elephant Gang at his back.

If Little Italy wished to survive that raid, it would need to mobilise its forces. The prospect brought him no pleasure at all. After the last caller had departed he put on his black pyjamas and, still wearing his check-cap, went to bed.

His world had been changed, and he sensed that for him life would never be quite the same again. He silently cursed the fate that had taken him to the Griffin and wondered whether he would pay for this night's work with his life. He was still wondering when he fell asleep.

2

THE IMPREGNABLE FORTRESS

*"My son, God has given you great power. You
will have to decide whether that gift is to be used
for good or evil" — Father James Delaney,
speaking to Darby Sabini.*

As always on a Sunday, Darby rose at seven. An odd
contradiction this for a man who had slept away the other
mornings of his life. He boiled some water on the stove and
shaved with a cut-throat, noting with satisfaction that there
were no marks from the night before. He had always been
worried about going to Mass with a bruised face.

His wife Maria was busy frying bacon. She was already
heavy with their first child and at thirty, plump, homely and
sprouting a faint moustache.

It was while they were eating breakfast together that he
said, "Tomorrow I am putting the house in your name and
that of your unborn child."

"Why," she asked with a laugh, "do you expect to die
soon?"

He shrugged by way of an answer, no trace of a smile on
his own face, and suddenly she sobered. He saw the fear in
her eyes and misunderstood the cause.

He had always despised weakness and so there was a
trace of scorn in his voice as he said, "You have no cause for
alarm. Even the Elephant Gang don't wage war on women
and children."

She didn't answer because she was frightened, not of any
marauding mob, but of her husband. Darby was thirty-one.
She had known him for most of his adult years and had

always believed that she understood him. But now suddenly she had come to realise that she barely knew him at all.

He had always been gentle towards her, always reasonable, always kind. And she had come to accept his indolence, his lack of ambition, as an essential part of his character. She had told herself many times that she'd married a dreamer, but at least a dreamer of harmless dreams. Now he was shedding that image like a cloak and changing visibly before her eyes into a man who radiated some dangerous force.

He had always believed that for every man there is a certain destiny; and although his new role was not one he would have chosen willingly, he had no wish to quarrel with fate. During the space of a long night, he had come to accept the mantle of kingship. He could see nothing incongruous in the notion of a drifter who had avoided work like the plague suddenly being elevated to the position of saviour to an entire community on the stength of a bar-room brawl.

So when he walked down Saffron Hill with the black-clad Maria clinging to his arm, he accepted the respectful salutations of neighbours casually enough.

He wore the same rig as always. A dark suit of some coarse material, a shirt without a collar, a black muffler and a cap. But today the shoes had been shone, the suit brushed, the muffler ironed, and his cap sat square upon his head. No piratical tilt on a Sunday. Only a blind man could have failed to spot the change that had come to Little Italy. The young dandies were lined up two-deep outside St Peter's Catholic Church waiting to have their high-heeled boots buffed at the shoeshine stalls. Backs were stiffer and heads held higher. Pride had come tiptoeing home like an errant child.

For the first time in living memory the church was full. But Darby was ushered to a pew immediately in front of the pulpit which had clearly been set aside for the Sabini family. His brothers Harryboy, George, Joe and Fred, big handsome fellows, were already there.

When Mass was over the parish priest, Father James Delaney, walked down the aisle and no one else moved. They were all waiting for Darby to lead the way out into the sunlight, and gravely he did just that. Father Delaney, a square, grey-haired man not long over from Ireland, was waiting for him in the porch. He took the big, swollen right hand of Darby and studied it with a slight smile.

"My son," he said, "God has given you a great power. You will have to decide whether that gift is to be used for good or evil."

Maria, not really understanding, was flushed with pride. Darby lowered his head and said not a word. That day there was wine on every table. The Italians were already celebrating the change in their fortunes; and only Darby realised just how fragile were those hopes.

Massarda was also celebrating after his fashion. Once again he had Jeannie stretched out naked across the bed. Only this time it was different. He was in the mood, still exultant from Darby's already famous victory of the night before; and when this feeling was upon him, all women were beautiful.

"We are the ones," he said. "Soon you'll be proud to say you've been bedded by one of the Sabinis. It will be like a badge for you. Not Raddies, Gits or Eyeties any more. Just Sabinis."

He was only half joking. With him, the dream was always close to the reality. There were just two things he did well in life, driving fast cars and making love, and it wasn't because like so many men he needed the sense of machismo. It was just that he sensed a beauty in the fast cars and the fast women that he could find nowhere else.

He loved all the variations of women, the gentle and the fiery ones, the plump and the lean. He had made love to more women than even he could remember, and yet when the passion was upon them, he had never known two to be entirely the same.

Now he was concentrating all his attention upon Jeannie and, for the moment, she was beautiful too. Her breathing became faster, the look in her eyes more rapt; and then because he was a man who liked to take his time, he stopped.

"Only a Sabini makes love as good as this," he said.

Jeannie was happy enough for an excuse to talk, if only to damp down the fires that were being lit by the talented fingers of Massarda.

"Last night you were an Italian. Tonight you're a Sabini. Do you really believe that one punch can change the world, that your gold-toothed friend can scare off every tearaway that comes hunting for trouble in Little Italy?"

Massarda answered with a seriousness foreign to his nature. "Darby won't be alone next time. Fellows around here have been running scared for so long that they never gave themselves the chance to stop and think. It wasn't that they were cowards, just losers. They never believed they had a chance, so they kept on running. But all they ever needed was a leader and now they've got Darby. They know he'll stand and fight. No one will ever run Darby off. He's the one man who can give them back their pride."

"And how about you? Will he give you back your pride?"

Massarda chuckled. "I'm different," he said. "I never lost mine. I've been too busy pleasuring twitchy little showgirls like you."

Darby had left school at the age of twelve, barely able to read or write; and since then the only books he'd perused had been those concerned with the running of horses. He had no great gift for conversation, little knowledge of the outside world. Politics and economics concerned him not at all, for he was a simple man with simple tastes. Yet thirty years spent on the streets of Little Italy had given him a certain wisdom.

He had come to understand that there are doubts in the minds of all men, however strong, however self-assured they might appear to be; that if those doubts could be properly exploited, even the most formidable fellows could become like putty in the hand. He understood that even cold men can be warm, and warm men cold; that the most respectable God-fearing men have their vices; that the most villainous can be capable of love. He understood that greed, envy, lust, deceit and fear are common ground to all men. And realising the vulnerability of his fellow-humans, he was careful not to allow his own true emotions to show upon his face.

He knew that most men meeting him for the first time regarded him as an Italian peasant, a simple fellow if not totally a fool. He was happy to be so regarded. Yet this simple Italian peasant had an ability to plan military campaigns, to out-manoeuvre the enemy, that would have put four-star generals to shame. And he now put this talent to work.

Three public houses, the Yorkshire Grey, the Bull and the Griffin, formed the frontiers of Little Italy; and Darby elected to use these as the headquarters for his army. They thus served a dual purpose. They were look-out posts from which strangers coming into the territory could be observed. And they were also points from which his soldiers could be summoned at the first sign of trouble. It was his desire to turn Little Italy into an impregnable fortress. But he knew this would take time and, with the Elephant Gang already on a warlike footing, that was a commodity in short supply.

He chose his men carefully. He didn't want a band of miscellaneous tearaways like the Elephant Gang, or the temperamental violence of the Birmingham Boys in which the rank and file organised constant coups against the leaders and discipline was almost non-existent. So first of all he built a hard core of fighting men around him. They were recruited from the ring and were equally adept on the cobbles.

The qualities that Darby prized above all others in his fellow-men were gameness and loyalty; and the need for these governed all his choices in that inner circle.

The first signing was Angelo Ginicoli, who had fought professionally under the name of George Thomas of

Clerkenwell. He had come home on leave from France during the war, gone on the run and fought as 'Bill Shelton's Unknown'. He later carved out a ring reputation as George Langham.

Darby next enlisted Fred Gilbert, a welterweight with a solid punch and a speedy left hand whose wife sold flowers in the Clerkenwell Road. During the war, he had also deserted and changed his name to Fred Clancey.

In his search for handy fighters, Darby didn't have to look far. In the next street from Saffron Hill lived Pasquala Poppa, a sturdy young bantamweight who later became known as Bert Marsh. He had been good enough to put Pete Herman on the floor during sparring before Herman's bout with Jimmy Wilde for the flyweight championship of the world.

Then one night at the Blackfriars Ring, Darby watched a thickset, completely bald lightweight from Bloomsbury named Jimmy Ford put down a heavier opponent in ferocious style. Next day he too was invited to join the mob and accepted the offer.

This quartet together with Massarda and Darby's brothers, Fred and Joe Sabini, formed the nucleus of a band of orthodox fighters who were to become virtually unbeatable in hand-to-hand battles.

Darby also gathered a group of men who looked highly impressive in the crowd scenes ... bit players who would fill out a squad to menacing proportions, but who actually did very little and consequently could be paid smaller fees. This group included a character known only as Big Tex who supplemented his income by posing for artists; Danny Gray, a rather half-hearted professional boxer who became a singer on the London music-hall stage; Big Harry Mansfield, a fighter who had a brief career in America; and Dai Thomas, a boxer from Wales.

He chose Alf White as his counsellor and used Alfie Solomons, a Jewish tearaway from Covent Garden, on a freelance basis.

This squad was backed up by the tool merchants. The

flick knife had yet to be invented and when it was, the Italians scorned it. They were the exponents of the razor, preferring the cut-throat variety bound with adhesive tape so that only the last inch of the blade was exposed.

Darby had a purist dislike of razor-slashing and yet was wise enough to accept it as an unfortunate necessity in his new line of work. Although he would send razor teams in pursuit of his enemies, he always walked away when the cutting began.

But the bit of team-building for which Darby would be given the most credit in years to come came about by chance towards the close of a hot summer evening. Strolling into the Griffin, he had been surprised to find a band of Italian teenagers bellying up to the bar. He ordered them out into the street.

Only the previous week, he had decreed that no Italian under the age of twenty-one should sup in the bars of Little Italy. He thus displayed a fine disregard for the laws of the land, which defined eighteen as the legal age. The boys left hurriedly. Ever since the cradle they had become accustomed to obeying the dictates of their elders. However, one boy, a dark and saturnine lad named Nino Zoff, made no move to go. He continued to sip his ale in leisurely fashion, and when he raised his eyes, they were cool and unafraid.

"Let me ask you a question," said the boy. "Why should I obey your laws rather than theirs," and he nodded in the direction of the Gray's Inn Road police station which was no more than a stone's-throw from the Griffin. "You are not my father nor even part of my family. You have never bound me with any act of kindness. In all the years I have seen you walk on by, you have never once stopped and spoken a single word to me. So tell me why you now deny me the right to have a quiet drink with money earnt by honest toil."

The words had been spoken in a voice of reason as though Nino was seeking the answer to a riddle.

Darby was amused by the boy's temerity, but he chose to reply gravely. "Tell me what that law across the street has ever done for your father or for your friends. Has it helped your mother to sleep more safely in her bed? Did it find the ruffians who split open your Uncle Fredo's head?"

He paused and when Nino stayed silent, continued, "But if I should become the law, those ruffians would be punished and your mother, your sister and all the women in Little Italy would be safer. And when you finally become a man, you would walk a little straighter and take pride in being called an Italian."

And then with a sudden change of mood, he took the boy's arm and moved him to a quiet corner of the room. "But I can see you're a sensible young fellow who would come to no harm from having a drink. You have already learnt the art of moderation. I would make an exception in your case if I could. But how can I? If you came into the Griffin, those other young bucks would come in too. They lack your discretion. They would soon give us all a bad name. So let us do each other a service."

At that Darby lowered his head and spoke softly into the ear of Nino. Eventually they shook hands and the boy walked out into the street. Darby watched him go with a thoughtful eye.

3

BATTLE OF THE NILE

"Next time you take guns down to the Nile, make sure you've got some real men behind them" —
Georgie Sewell's challenge to the Sabinis.

Darby had taken precautions against every eventuality. His planning was faultless, his security impeccable. He had been patient, hoping to use the full year to prepare. But he was not to get his necessary year because fate itself took a stand against him.

It had all begun with a minor affray outside a West End gambling club. Jimmy Jones, a member of the Titanic Mob from Hoxton, had been placed on the door with orders to keep the Sabinis out; and when Alfie Solomons, Jimmy Ford and Sandy Rice arrived one night, Jimmy Jones did just that. Blows were struck. Some men from Hoxton who were in the club joined in. Eventually the Sabinis were driven away, but threatened to return. On subsequent nights the club was bulging with Titanic mobsters anxious to teach the Raddies a lesson, but the Sabinis stayed away.

They did so on the orders of Darby. He had no wish to get involved in a battle in the West End where everybody's hand, including that of the police, would be against them. Yet he also knew he couldn't ignore the incident. He had taken great pains to build up the confidence and the pride of his men; but after the long years of humiliation, this was still a fragile thing.

He couldn't run the risk of having it dented at this early stage of the game. So in the manner of an urban guerrilla leader, he decided to strike where least expected … in the Albion public house, known as the 'Blood Tub', in the heart of Hoxton.

This was one of the headquarters of the Titanics, and he knew that several of the gang were bound to be there at any given hour of the day. So early on a Friday evening, Darby and a detachment of about twenty men left the Griffin and moved off in a motorised cavalcade along the Clerkenwell Road eastwards in the direction of Hoxton.

There were at least ten guns in the party, a basket of ammunition in the back of Massarda's Bugatti, and a spirit of high adventure. But the element of surprise which Darby had relied upon was not forthcoming. A member of the Sabinis with strong family ties in Hoxton had caught a cab half an hour earlier to warn the Titanics of the Italians' approach. Consequently the Titanics were armed and ready when the Sabini cavalcade rolled up Nile Street towards the Albion. Jimmy Bond, who had been decorated in France in a different kind of shooting war, assumed command and placed ten gunmen behind upturned market stalls along a fifty-yard length of Nile Street. Other gunmen were placed in the Albion, which commanded a view west along Nile Street.

But Darby had sent one car through the back streets, and suddenly the door of the Blood Tub burst open and an Italian tearaway known as Boffa emptied two chambers of a revolver into the polished bar front, a foot or so from where Bond was standing.

The remaining Sabinis took cover behind a line of fruit barrows on the other side of the street and began firing energetically through the wheels. Harry Bargery, a Titanic mobster known as 'Bargee', spun to the ground clutching a shattered wrist, and Bob Simpson who went to his aid also got a bullet in the arm from the Colt which Massarda was firing from the protection of an obelisk.

Jimmy Jones, summoned from the nearby King of Prussia, skirted behind the Sabini lines, grabbed Boffa by the neck and laid him cold with a length of lead pipe

Boffa was dragged across the road to the Titanic stalls where he was set upon by the Titanic women led by Lizzie Chandler, Bargee's wife. They began stripping the clothes from the still barely conscious body, while giving him a vicious beating. More vengeful than their menfolk, they would doubtless have killed him if Jimmy Bond hadn't intervened. He didn't want cold-blooded murder on his patch.

Five minutes after the shooting had started, it was all over. At the sound of the approaching police bells, the firing stopped. Darby hustled his men into their cars.

Double Handsome, so named because he was the ugliest of all the Titanics, hurried to collect the Titanic guns and hide them. The wounded men were helped to a nearby house. And only Boffa, lying behind an upturned stall, bore mute testimony to the affray. The police wanted to claim him, but the Titanic women insisted that he was merely an innocent passer-by who had somehow got caught in the crossfire. Knowing the impossibility of obtaining evidence once gangland had closed its ranks, the police shrugged and left him lying there, confident that as soon as they'd gone the Sabinis would come and collect him.

Darby, riding back through Clerkenwell Green, his gun still warm in his back pocket, considered the evening a fair success. Two men with minor flesh wounds and Boffa, whose head was hard, were the Sabinis' tally of casualties.

He had given strict orders beforehand that no man should shoot to kill. This had only been intended as a token warning, a reminder that the Italians could no longer be insulted lightly. The Sabinis were now a force to be reckoned with, and he knew that by nightfall this message would have been relayed loud and clear to the other London gangs. But he was acute enough to realise that he had been betrayed by one of his own band, and this knowledge troubled him greatly.

Big Alf White was troubled too. He slept badly that night. In the morning, he rose early as always and prepared a cooked breakfast for his children. His wife, who ran the family florist business, departed with every dawn to buy the flowers in nearby Covent Garden.

After the children had gone to school, he padded around the house in his old bathrobe and red felt slippers as he pondered on the day's work that lay ahead of him. He had no illusions about his position in the Sabini camp. The Italians regarded him as a stranger, even worse as a foreigner, and could never understand why Darby had chosen him in the first place. Now that they knew they had a traitor in the camp, he was the automatic suspect, and not just because he was an Englishman. The long-time leader of the Titanics was a small, carefully dressed man named Charlie Wooder and known to his associates as 'The Kid'. By an unfortunate chance, Charlie Wooder was Alf White's brother-in-law.

White knew that but for the steadying hand of Darby he might already be a dead man. With passions running high after the Hoxton raid, some of the Sabini firebrands had wanted White brought before a kangaroo court where sentence would have been followed by summary bloody justice. Darby had quelled that notion by the use of the simple logic for which he was fast becoming famous.

"Tell me," he had said, "do you consider Big Alf a foolish fellow?"

It was almost a rhetorical question. White, one of the few college-educated gangsters of the twenties, was celebrated for his astuteness. This was naturally why Darby had chosen him as his counsellor.

So the firebrands admitted readily enough that of all the adjectives they might have used to describe Big Alf, foolish wouldn't have been one.

Darby shrugged. "Then wouldn't you say he must have suffered a very sudden change of character to have turned traitor over such a matter ... knowing that suspicion would automatically fall upon him? Tell me, wouldn't that have been the act of a very foolish fellow indeed?"

That question too was unanswerable, and yet White knew that his life was still balanced on the razor's edge. If

Darby should decide that White was after all his betrayer, there would be no place left to hide. He would be hunted down like a wild thing.

So he used that celebrated intelligence and his equally celebrated contacts to track down the true traitor, and by early afternoon he had the name. It was Fred Gilbert, who had been a member of Darby's trusted inner ring and a man with strong family ties in Hoxton.

He was immediately summoned before Darby in the Griffin. He was a sturdy fellow who had many times shown his gameness in the ring, but on this occasion there was a pale, haunted look about his face. The kind of look you see on men who sense that they may be close to death. But Darby showed no outward signs of anger.

"We have known each other a long time, Fred," he said, "and I've always trusted you. So tell me the truth now like the honest fellow you are and I'll believe you. Were you the one who went to Hoxton before the guns?"

The question wasn't as naive as it might have sounded. Darby already knew that Gilbert had been in Hoxton that day. What he didn't know was why. Any denial would instantly have branded him as guilty.

Gilbert looked Darby square in the eye. "Yes, I went to Hoxton," he said, "but not to warn them. I would swear that on my mother's life. As you know, we have friends near the Nile and my wife was visiting them that afternoon. I became worried about her safety and so thought it best to collect her before the shooting started."

Darby had been watching him thoughtfully during this speech. He was wondering whether a man who had known about the raid since the early morning of that day would have allowed his wife to visit Hoxton in the first place. Or indeed whether the wife herself had carried the warning. But none of this showed in his face.

"It's my fault, Fred, not yours," he said. "I placed you in an impossible position. If my own wife had been in the Nile that day, I would have behaved as you behaved. I would have gone down there and collected her. A man who neglects his family is no man at all."

He shrugged. "But you must see that with these divided loyalties of yours, you can be of no further use to me. My friends' enemies become my enemies, but how could you feel that when you already have two sets of friends at war with one another?

"No, it just wouldn't be fair to ask you to stay with us. Every time something like this happened you would be suspect. So it is better that you go now before that can happen. You just walk out of that door and no one will lay a hand on you. You have my word on it."

Before leaving, Gilbert reached out a hand and after only a momentary hesitation Darby took it in both of his and smiled his gold smile.

Gilbert was reassured by the hand-clasp and the smile; unaware of the fact that Darby was merely making the classical tactical move to gain the victim's trust. A week later, he sent a team of razor-slashers after Gilbert. They cornered him on Sandown racecourse; and left him disfigured and crippled for life.

The Sabinis celebrated their first foray into rival territory with a full-scale Italian party at the Fratalanza Club in Great Bath Street. Long tables were piled high with spicy food and gallon jugs of black homemade wine. There were flowers everywhere and a small band thumped out the tunes of Old Italy.

The younger men stamped their feet in time with the mandolin's wild strumming. And every now and then the Italian matrons would take the floor with their partners and dance side by side, arms around one another's waists, Mediterranean style.

The younger girls just stood and watched. They were mostly second-generation Italians who had lost touch with the customs of their kinsfolk.

Most of the men who had taken part in the raid were there, standing a little apart from the rest. Massarda was smiling, running his eyes over the girls who had come unescorted. Ginicoli and Pasquala Poppa were listening earnestly to Darby. And at the far end of the bar Georgie Sewell, alone by choice, nursed a drink and watched the room with those cold, sharp eyes of his.

He was said to be the most dapper man in the underworld, and tonight it was easy to see how he'd gained that reputation. He had the look of a prosperous stockbroker. His dark-blue pinstripe was immaculate. You could have shaved in the shine of his shoes. His light-brown hair was neatly brushed. A diamond stickpin glittered on his shirt front, and on the bar beside him lay the bowler with the upturned brim that travelled with him everywhere. The crown had been specially reinforced to help absorb the impact of truncheons and cudgels alike.

Darby watched him uneasily, wondering why he had chosen to come to the party. Sewell had spent much of his youth in Clerkenwell and his sister had married an Italian named Johnny Rossini. But although he had shown a certain respect for Darby, he had no love at all for the other Italians or they for him.

He had taken no part in the affray; but if he had taken sides, he would most likely have backed the Titanics. He had friends in Hoxton. However, it was typical of the man that he had come uninvited to a party where his very life could be in danger.

The Cobblestone Fighter was the only man in the world who could make Darby nervous. The man was like a natural force, not truly subject to control. He had to be handled as gingerly as dynamite. But it was more than the mere physical threat that worried Darby. He had always made a point of trying to understand his fellow-men; because he was convinced that once you fully understood a man, there could be nothing to fear. You could anticipate his every move, exploit the weaknesses, sidestep the strengths. But try as he might Darby couldn't understand this cold-eyed frightener.

For a start he couldn't understand the fierce pride that forced him over and over again to go up against armed men with only his bare hands as weapons. The price of that pride was already a network of scars across the face. By the time he was forty Sewell would need no fewer than three hundred and twenty-two stitches to hold his tough hide together.

Darby had his own pride and a pathological hatred of razors, but ever since his clash with the Trimmer he'd been carrying a gun, a Webley and Scott automatic. This was the revolver issued to the Metropolitan Police and one that carried eight rounds. To Darby, it had become as constant a companion as the cap and the black muffler.

Most of all, Darby was puzzled by Sewell's attitude to the world around him. He was by any standards a violent criminal who had taken part in some of the most daring heists the city had ever known; and there seemed a distinct possibility that one day those fearsome hands of his would kill a man. Yet he had an odd respect for honest men and his enemies were invariably frighteners in the same line of work. There was something in Sewell's dark nature that forced him to pick up every challenge, every insult, however small, and exact retribution.

Darby was still thinking about this when Alfie Solomons, already half drunk on unfamiliar wine and the admiration of the young bucks, confronted Sewell. "We were looking for you today, Georgie, down on the Nile, wondering which team you'd be with. But then of course that isn't your kind of thing, is it? They tell me you don't know how to use a tool."

Solomons clearly believed he was safe with the mob around him. His words were tipped with malice.

"I don't," admitted the Cobblestone Fighter, "and I'm proud of that fact. Any half-assed little impostor can build himself a reputation by waving a shooter around. But it takes a man to use his hands."

He had a very quiet voice for such a violent man. And then he smiled at Solomons as if this was some private joke only he could appreciate. But since his eyes didn't smile, and since his outward character was so masked, the sudden change of his expression was chilling.

Solomons was half-dragged away by some of his companions and began drinking even more heavily than before. Darby, in the role of peacemaker, came to stand beside Sewell. "Too much wine and too many women can put foolish ideas in the head of a man. But in the morning he will come round and apologise to you, Georgie. I will make sure that he does."

Sewell shrugged as though the whole affair was of no account, but Darby wasn't fooled for a moment. He knew that Sewell with his prickly pride had already measured his man, and that it could now be only a matter of time before he exacted his vengeance.

He didn't have long to wait. Some half an hour later Solomons, in a mood of near madness, broke away from the clutching hands of his companions and advanced upon Sewell with a gun in his hand.

Women screamed and men shouted as he levelled the gun at Sewell's head in a vainglorious bid to put a touch of fear into those cold eyes.

Sewell still appeared to be the calmest man in the room. He placed his drink upon the bar almost casually, looked over Solomons' shoulder as though about to address a friend, and in that selfsame moment crossed his right hand to the chin. The punch was so short, so fast, that men standing just a few yards away never saw it land. But Solomons was already unconscious by the time he hit the floor.

By the tenets of gangland, Sewell would have been within his rights to have put the boot in. However, to the surprise of the Sabinis he made no attempt to do so. This had nothing to do with a sense of fair play and even less to do with kindness. It was merely that Sewell had realised that the best way to shame Solomons in the eyes of the crowd was to make it all look easy. He took the gun from Solomons' limp hand and gave it to Darby with a contemptuous shrug.

"Next time you take guns down to the Nile," he said,

"make sure you've got some real men behind them."

And with that he walked out of the Fratalanza. He didn't once look back …

Strippers by the very nature of their profession usually have firm young bodies and firm young breasts. They have dancers' legs and bored eyes that had lost their innocence long before the first G-string fell. They are medium-sized girls with medium-sized ambitions who live in fear of the pimp's knock upon the door.

Rose Patrick wasn't like that at all. Rose stood six-foot-one, weighed thirteen and a half stone, had the thighs and shoulders of a wrestler, and a right-hand punch good enough to drop a man in his tracks. Rose didn't fear anything or anyone in the whole wide world. All of which was just as well, for she had a job most other showgirls would have avoided like the plague.

Rose stripped at the stag nights of the London gangs; for the Broad Mob, the Treacle Plaster Mob, the Titanics, the Cortesis, and for other masters of mayhem too numerous to mention.

Tonight she was performing for the benefit of the Trimmer and his mates in a cellar club at the Elephant and Castle. And as she stripped she continued to exchange pleasantries with the crowd. She was walking a perilous path and she knew that, but her earthy good humour and total fearlessness were her shield. She was also well aware of the fact that men on such occasions as this are always a little alarmed at being singled out from the crowd. That knowledge gave her a certain power.

She slipped off her G-string, picked up a swagger cane, the kind that drill sergeants use, and began to high kick her way across the front of the stage. This was the highlight of her act, part of a game that only she would have dared to play.

She was virtually inviting the hands to reach out in a bid to grab a leg and pull her off the stage. She defended herself with the swagger cane, swatting the wrists and knuckles of the unruly, while continuing to taunt them in the most carefree way.

However, she had no illusions about her fate should she indeed be pulled into the crowd. It had happened twice before in other places, and each time a form of mob fever had run through the ranks. Eventually she had fought her way back on to the stage, breathless, bruised, but devoid of moral outrage. It was after all the line of work she'd chosen and she knew the risks. Tonight the mood was good-humoured enough and the sight of men hopping about, nursing smarting knuckles, repeatedly sent laughter rippling around the room.

But one man named Alex Jackson never even smiled. He was known throughout the London underworld as "Mad Alex" and he accepted the tag as a compliment, although it was never intended as such. He had spent three years in an asylum and now had one major passion in life. He enjoyed hurting people, preferably women.

Rose rapped another pair of knuckles and laughed; and it was that laugh which wiped away the last remnants of sanity from the twilight world of Mad Alex. The reality and the dream became mingled into one.

He burst through the front row and leapt for the stage. The suddenness of the attack had taken her by surprise and his hand fastened cruelly on to Rose's breast. But she had the instincts of a street fighter. Alex was still trying to scramble upon the stage, still trying to gain purchase for his legs. And so before he had a chance to recover his balance, she smashed her knee full into his face, forcing him to break his grip. Continuing the same movement, she placed her foot flat against his chest, gave a powerful shove and sent him toppling back into the crowd.

The blood was pumping from his mashed nose and the skin under his cheekbones had been turned purple by his anger; but still she couldn't resist the temptation to taunt him.

"If you don't mind your bloody manners, Alex," she said, "we'll have to get Darby to give you a spanking."

He would have rushed the stage again if strong hands hadn't held him back. His voice was a frustrated wail, "Tomorrow night Darby will be a dead man. And, you lousy bitch, you won't live long enough to bury him."

Before he could say more the big fist of the Trimmer knocked him senseless. It was that blow from the Trimmer which truly underlined the meaning of the message. He wasn't the kind to concern himself with the safety of a woman. But careless talk which threatened a long-awaited revenge was something else again. The Elephant Gang were ready to make their move, and Darby would know within the hour.

It was a mark of Darby's astuteness that he had already set up a network of informers who could infiltrate the ranks of the other London gangs. Rose Patrick had been one of his first choices; for he knew that in the presence of such women, most men are apt to become foolish and loose-tongued.

4

RETURN OF THE TRIMMER

"Let him go, boys. He's of more use to us alive
with the marks on him than he is dead" —
Nino Zoff's words of wisdom.

Anne Marlowe was relaxing in the sunken marble tub of her Mayfair apartment. Far below the traffic rattled its way along Park Lane. But in this silken eyrie, the sounds of the city could have been a million miles away. She rubbed the rich soap into a perfumed lather over her body, the movements of her hands slow and sensuous; and with the bubbles still clinging to her, she rose and directed the needlepoint spray of the shower over every suntanned inch.

Then stepping out of the tub, she caught her reflection in the floor-to-ceiling mirror. She studied herself carefully. She didn't look her twenty-eight years. She was still slim, still straight. Her jet-black hair had retained the bounce and shine of youth, and her flesh was smooth to the touch. In her teens, she had been a favourite pin-up of the stage magazines, and if anything the passing years had only added to the allure.

She gave her reflection one final slow survey and nodded as though in answer to a question. She liked to stand there as now, naked, looking out over the rooftops of the city; knowing that at best she could be little more than a distant silhouette to her fellow Londoners.

From this eagle's nest, she could look into the gardens of Buckingham Palace. To the north, the smoke from the factories of St Albans smudged the sky; but on a clear day such as this, she could still see the Crystal Palace glinting in the sunlight.

However, most of all she liked to watch the people walking in the park. She knew that the women, mainly the younger ones, envied her fame and fortune. She was, after all, one of the beautiful people; always exquisitely gowned, forever riding in the back of chauffeur-driven limousines, the darling of first-night audiences. But the truth was that there were times when she would gladly have changed places with each and every one of those women who walked daily through the parks. She was envious of the unseen infants being wheeled along in the perambulators, of the families wrapped around them, and above all else she was envious of their freedom.

For no prisoner was ever guarded more zealously than Anne Marlowe. She was the plaything of theatre magnate James Frazer, who gave her everything except love. He had first spotted her in the chorus line at the Lyceum. She had been sweet seventeen and he thought she was the most beautiful thing he'd ever seen. So he bought her in much the same fashion as he'd bought all the other possessions he'd desired along the way.

He made her a star. He surrounded her with luxury, but he was a frugal man who always made sure that his investments paid a rich dividend. And Anne Marlowe had paid a very rich dividend indeed. The shows in which she'd starred had almost doubled his fortune, and in return he had really given her very little. The apartment she lived in, the chauffeur-driven Rolls, even much of the jewellery she wore, still belonged to him.

She was constantly spied upon. The doorman in the apartment block made weekly reports of all the visitors she'd received and just how long they had remained with her. If a man stayed for more than half an hour, Frazer would demand to know the reason why.

In the beginning he had slept with her three nights each week before returning to his aristocratic wife in the country for the long weekends. But it had always been a cold-hearted kind of love-making. She had been little more than a high-priced whore servicing her one and only client. And so in all of her twenty-eight years, she had never known a true lover, never known a single moment of wild, unbridled passion; and yet she grieved for such moments more fiercely than any lover in any romance.

She could of course have found herself a lover. Every day she encountered men who made it clear without actually saying a word that they would be delighted to bed the beautiful Anne Marlowe.

But she had no doubt at all that Frazer would learn of any such sexual adventure within the hour. He wouldn't beat her up or have the legs of her lover broken. He was far too civilised for that. He would simply take back the apartment, the Rolls and the stardom. He was powerful enough to do that and, at twenty-eight, she was very vulnerable.

She had just finished towelling herself when the doorbell chimed. She slipped on a robe and opened the door to find Frazer standing there; and for a moment there was something close to disappointment in her eyes. And then as if to cover up that reaction, she smiled quickly.

"Come on in, darling," she said and led the way into the lounge.

He had been away in New York for the past six weeks; but even so she was surprised when he took her in his arms and kissed her with an enthusiasm he hadn't shown for years.

But as he broke away he was already frowning, looking at his watch. "I almost forgot," he said, "I have to be at the Savoy for lunch."

He poured himself a drink and added by way of explanation, "It's business." Then he left. There were no presents and he didn't even kiss her goodbye.

The Trimmer made his return to the Griffin in style, at the head of a cavalcade of Elephant Gang staff cars and with thirty strong-arm men behind him. They drove past the Griffin and parked near the Gray's Inn police station in

Theobalds Road. One of the Italian boys ran from the coffee stall into the Griffin to tell Darby the news. His brothers, Joe, Fred and Harryboy, stood by his side at the bar and there were maybe half-a-dozen other men in the room who might have been expected to support him. Even so he could only hope to muster ten men at most which meant that he was outnumbered three to one by the hand-picked toughs of the Trimmer.

Darby spoke quietly to the boy who left the bar even faster than he'd entered it a moment ago. However, it was clear that if he had gone to fetch reinforcements from the Bull and the Yorkshire Grey, he would need winged feet. The Trimmer was already crossing the road towards the Griffin. He was smiling as he came through the door, scarcely able to credit his good fortune in finding the four brothers cut off from the main band.

He spotted Carmen Cardoza and pointed a thick forefinger in her direction, unable to resist the grandstand gesture.

"You see, we haven't forgotten you," he shouted. "Once we've finished with this lot, we'll be taking you back with us south of the river. What you might call spoils of bloody war." And he laughed at his own joke.

It was Darby who struck the first blow, flattening a man with a single punch. Then there was blood and shouting and women screaming as they hurried for the door. It began as a fist fight, a token fixture without a razor in sight; but no one had any illusions about that. This was simply a standard tactic of gangland battles in public places. The Elephant Gang had death and destruction in mind, but that would only come on the cobbles and in the alleyways in front of witnesses with forgetful minds. And with that notion, the Trimmer and his friends began to drag the Sabinis out into the street. Darby took three of them with him in a sprawling whirl of arms and legs.

The action was so fast and furious that for a moment no one saw Nino emerge from behind the awning of the coffee stall with a small army of Italian teenagers behind him, a knife in every hand.

They began to advance as though on slippered feet and the silence was more menacing than words could ever have been. The Elephant Gang made a run for their cars, but they never really had a chance. The boys, more fleet-footed, were slashing at them every step along the way.

The Trimmer's haunches were the prime target for Nino, anxious to show that he took any threat to Darby very personally indeed. But when the Trimmer fell just a few feet short of the cars, Nino still had the wit to save him from almost certain death as his by now blood-crazed band began to cluster around the big man.

"Let him go, boys," ordered Nino, the only calm one in sight. "He's of more use to us alive with the marks on him than he is dead."

Darby considered this rare wisdom for one so young. For he knew that although the police were quite happy to turn a blind eye towards a gang battle, they couldn't possibly ignore murder. He knew too that the Trimmer was indeed worth more to him alive than dead. He was mute testimony to the fact that Little Italy with the Sabinis backed by Nino's army was now impregnable.

The band at the Stardust was playing 'I Only Have Eyes For You' and Anne Marlowe was dancing with Alexander Levine. She wasn't enjoying the experience. Levine was said to be one of the three richest men in the world. He owned tanker fleets, film companies, banks and some of the finest racehorses in Europe. He was also very fat, very drunk and a first-class son of a bitch. His paunch bumped her lecherously and his hand roamed freely from bare shoulder to rounded rump. In his experience, women would suffer just about any kind of indignity from a millionaire.

Not for the first time Anne cursed the day James Frazer had bought the Stardust. To him, it could never be just another club. It was intended as a monument to his success, a constant reminder of his triumphs. He didn't court the Beautiful People. That had never been his game. He was interested only in the men of power, the tycoons, the politicians and his fellow theatre magnates, all of whom were now only too anxious to rub shoulders with the high and mighty Frazer. It gave him an almost sensual pleasure to remember that he had left school at twelve, barely able to read or write, and still travelled so far.

He continued to regard Anne Marlowe as a bauble picked up along the way. A very decorative bauble, but just the same a bauble that would one day grow too old and have to be replaced. However, for the moment she had her uses. Her beauty and her fame continued to fill his theatres and at the Stardust she acted as hostess to the men of power. He had his own private table at the club for his chosen guests, and at this she presided.

She smiled at their tired old jokes. She listened to their stories and hid the boredom in her eyes. She danced when they wished to dance and pretended not to notice their careless hands. For this was one of Frazer's odd double standards. He would allow no man to bed or steal his paramour; but he gained a certain pleasure from the knowledge that she was desired by his friends. Provided they were discreet, they could touch but not take.

Alexander Levine had long gone past the point of discretion. This may have been because he was so very rich that the standards of normal men didn't apply to him any more. And it may also have been because Frazer was spending the evening at his country home.

Three times Anne had moved that straying hand and each time her smile had grown a little more tired. Other diners had begun to watch them with some interest. "Please don't," she said, and she was still smiling.

He gave a fat man's chuckle, but the voice was harsh. "Don't play the innocent with me," he said. "James bought you a long time ago. I could treble that price without even thinking."

And so saying he lowered his hand once more to her rump, grasping the flesh lewdly with his fat fingers. Before he could progress further his shoulder was seized in a grip of iron and he was spun away from his partner. He turned full of fury to see the smiling face of Silvio Massarda.

"My dance, I believe," said Massarda, who looked as always the most good-natured of men. Only the grip of iron said otherwise. Before Levine could recover his poise, Massarda had taken Anne into his arms and danced away.

"You know this isn't an excuse-me," she said.

"Really!" replied Massarda, affecting surprise and then beginning to laugh. "Maybe someone should have told me."

She smiled, finding his happy-go-lucky nature infectious. "You're a rascal," she said.

Massarda shrugged. "You're right. I am. But at least I'm a rascal who rescued a princess from a fat dragon."

Massarada had been dining at the Stardust for weeks, waiting patiently for the chance to meet this woman of his dreams; and tonight his dreams had been answered. He would never be more welcome. But like the practised pursuer that he was, he had no intention of overplaying his hand. He stayed on the floor with her for just one more dance, chatting easily, lifting her spirits, deliberately restoring her pride. He danced in the old-fashioned way, almost at arm's length, and yet with the subtle grace of a Latin. When the music stopped he led Anne back to her table, kissed her hand and still smiling said, "Don't forget, Princess, any time you need me all you have to do is whistle."

Then almost as an afterthought he moved across to Levine and bending down whispered in his ear, words that he alone could hear. "If you ever lay so much as a finger on that lady again, my fat friend," he said, "I'll have your balls hanging from your ears."

Massarda was smiling even more broadly than before. But Anne Marlowe noticed that Levine had turned deathly pale.

Later that evening Darby returned to the Griffin, which was filled to overflowing with men anxious to celebrate the

"He set out with the intention of protecting his people. He ended up by creating a criminal empire the likes of which Britain had never seen before . . . and will almost certainly never see again." Scotland Yard Commander Jack Capstick speaking of Darby Sabini

"The underworld can have known few stranger friendships than this . . . a friendship between Darby Sabini (left), the most powerful gangster of his day, and Jack Capstick (above), a man who had dedicated his life to hunting down the villains"

The Saffron Hill gang, 1920. From the left: Unknown, Joe Sabini, Micky Papa, Paul Cortesi, Angelo Ginicoli, Harry Cortesi (in boater hat), Darby Sabini, Gus Cortesi, Unknown, Harryboy Sabini, George Cortesi

Georgie Sewell, the Cobblestone Fighter and his wife Hetty.
"In hand-to-hand fighting on the streets, he was considered
almost invincible"

Little Italy, 1907. "For hunters such as the Trimmer, here was the perfect hunting ground. You could beat up the men and rape the women in the certain knowledge that no one would ever complain to the police"

Sabinis' latest victory.

He was ushered through to the bar like a conquering hero. He stood there for a moment smiling, gold teeth glinting, and then in a fine Italian baritone he began to sing his favourite song 'Rosie Magoola':

"Rosie Magoola come around-a dis way, Rosie Magoola come around and she say, I'm going to show this little dance to you, Then right down the street she went, Shaking her feet as they do in Honolulu."

5

AN ACCIDENTAL AMBUSH

*"Give them another year and they'll own the South. We've got to stop them. It's now or never"
— Birmingham gang boss Billy Kimber making plans for war.*

Billy Kimber was an unusually civilised man to have been a gangster chief in the twenties. He enjoyed fine clothes and fine wines. He liked to dine in the very best restaurants, to mingle with first-night audiences, to converse with the intelligentsia. And when he wished he could be quite charming.

Then again when he wished, he could shed that sophistication like a cloak and become as cruel and ruthless as any mob enforcer. It was this mixture of intelligence and occasional brutality that had enabled him to become boss of the Birmingham Boys, sometimes known as the Brummagem Boys ... a motley collection of thugs based in Birmingham but recruited from far and wide. Billy had been raised in the Elephant and Castle area of London. So had several of his followers. Others came from Cardiff, Hoxton and of course Birmingham itself. The individual members had little in common, but were simply bound together by their prejudices. They hated Jews, they hated foreigners and they hated the Sabinis most of all.

It was a mark of Billy Kimber's talents that with such dubious backing he had become the premier power in the British underworld. For a decade and more he had controlled the racecourses. But now that the Sabinis had thrown down the gauntlet, his kingship was being seriously threatened for the first time.

Initially he hadn't taken the challenge too seriously. He had believed that Darby would be primarily concerned with the protection of Little Italy. He considered the Italian too indolent ever to be an empire builder, and thus looked upon this change of tactics as little more than a whim.

Perhaps for Darby it started that way. One night in the Griffin someone had mentioned that Sam Garvin, the Sheffield gang leader, was making a clear £12,000 from racing alone, and running a coach-built Bentley three-litre sports saloon.

"If Sam can make that sort of money belting people with a piece of lead," Darby had proclaimed, "I can make twice that and never touch anybody."

Kimber had perhaps forgotten that even the most indolent of men can become energetic when they are enjoying their work. And Darby loved the racing game. The race courses of England literally widened his horizons, taking him away from the narrow, all-confining streets of Little Italy.

He had been known to stand on top of the hill at Epsom, breathe deeply and then turn to his brother Harryboy, saying, "That's a brand of air you will never find in the city." Then having made his statement, he could continue to chain-smoke throughout the meeting, filling his lungs with good old-fashioned smoke.

In the space of a single year, the Sabinis had made their presence felt on all the major racecourses of Southern England, and for Billy Kimber this was a challenge that could no longer be ignored. He decided to ambush the Sabinis' lorry on its way home at the close of the Derby meeting, catching them unawares, outnumbered and unprepared for war.

He discussed the plan with two of his lieutenants, George Sage and Harry Brown, sometimes known as 'Mad Harry'. Brown, a messiah of violence, wrapped an arm around Kimber's shoulders. "This is what the boys have been waiting for," he said delightedly. "The chance to give those Raddie bastards a real hiding. By the time we've finished with them, they'll be cut to ribbons. The road will run red with their blood. We'll show them up for what they are, a bunch of impostors."

George Sage, who like Kimber had close links with the Elephant Gang, was more cautious. "Don't underrate Darby," he warned. "He may have that dreamy look about him, but he's smart and he's dangerous. If he's there, they'll stand and fight."

Kimber agreed. "They'll follow Darby Sabini anywhere. If he wants to go up, they'll go with him. Give them another year and they'll own the South. We've got to stop them. It's now or never."

But just for once it seemed as though Darby's famed powers of command were slipping. On the opening day of the Epsom meeting he was talking to some influential bookmakers when Big Tex accosted him.

Tex had been drinking steadily. "I'm skint," he said, slurring his words. "I need the money you owe and I need it now."

Darby sighed. "I'm a bit short at the moment, Tex, but I'll settle with you later. Now be a good fellow and go away."

But instead of going away, the big man put his hand on Darby's shoulder and gave him a shove. "Everyone knows your pockets are stuffed with fivers. So give me what's mine."

With the air of a man sorely tried, Darby reached into his top pocket and took out a single fiver. Tex promptly knocked it from his hand and let it flutter away on the breeze.

"It's a pony you owe me," he said, his voice rising. "I know you've always been mean. I didn't know you were a welsher too."

Darby stood there, the legendary patience all gone. "Pick it up," he said, "and we'll talk about this when you're sober."

It was then that Tex made the mistake of raising his fist as though about to strike the Italian.

Darby flattened him with a single punch and then turned to his companions. "Foolish fellows such as Tex," he explained, "mistake reason for weakness. Every now and then they have to be taught the error of their ways."

It was the look upon the faces of the bookmakers that gave him warning. Big Tex's chin had clearly been stronger than Darby had imagined. Now with a knife in his hand, and madness in his eyes, Tex was advancing upon his own gang leader.

Darby turned almost casually and just as casually swayed away from the slashing blade much in the same way as he'd once swayed away from punches in the ring. He seized Tex's wrist, forcing him to drop the knife, and then proceeded to give him a methodical beating, seemingly designed more to humiliate than disfigure. One final blow stretched out the big fellow upon the grass, and this time he didn't move.

Bert Marsh and several other Sabini soldiers had joined the watching crowd, ready to come to Darby's aid if the need arose.

Darby rubbed his grazed knuckles. "Take him away," he commanded, "he shames us all: and when he comes to, tell him that if I see him again during this meeting, I'll kill him."

It was said quietly, but the words were chilling just the same. Then Darby placed £25 (a pony) in Tex's pocket and stated defiantly, "I always pay my debts."

Tex paid attention to at least part of that warning. He steered well clear of Darby during the rest of the meeting. But he continued to drink heavily, utter vague threats and talk about injustices within the Sabini camp. Gangsters from all factions were wondering how Darby would finally decide to handle this rare bit of indiscipline within the ranks.

Otherwise the meeting went smoothly enough. The rival gangs from Birmingham, Leeds, Sheffield, Uttoxeter, Hoxton and Little Italy co-existed. There was hostility, but no bloodshed. And when the last race had been run on the Friday, they were in no great rush to hurry home. the bookmakers and their entourage (in this case, their protectors) were traditionally the last to leave. Stands had to be taken down, and there was a certain carnival air over the Downs.

The Leeds mob were the first to head for the car park, as they had the longest road to travel. There were curses when they discovered that their lorry wouldn't start. But just when it seemed as though they would be spending the night on the course, Big Tex came to their aid. Drawing mob leader Johnny Edmonds aside, he whispered, "Why don't you take the Sabinis' lorry? The keys are always left in the ignition. I know. I've driven it a time or two."

He paused, and there was something close to terror in his voice as he pleaded, "For God's sake, don't tell anyone it was my idea. If Darby ever finds out, I'm a dead man."

Billy Kimber and the more violent wing of the Birmingham Boys had taken up their positions just three miles away from the course near the Brick Kiln public house in Ewell. They had chosen their spot for an ambush well: a comparatively quiet stretch of road flanked by fields and at the top of a hill.

Mad Harry had been studying the oncoming traffic through a powerful pair of binoculars for the best part of an hour. Finally he spotted a large motor vehicle as it reached the foot of the hill. He focused for a long moment, then shouted out, "Here they come, boys. Remember, no mercy. We want to see the blood flow."

The approaching lorry, labouring under its load, rounded the bend at the top of the hill to find the road blocked by an empty coach. The occupants climbed down and were immediately set upon the Birmingham Boys armed with axes, hammers, cudgels, broken bottles, bars of iron, bricks, razors and coshes. It was carnage. The men on the lorry never had a chance. In the twilight, they couldn't even recognise their attackers, let alone guess the reason for such mayhem.

As Mad Harry had promised, the road was soon running red with blood. The Birmingham Boys were so high on their hatred of the Sabinis that all reason had flown. They just continued to hack at human flesh quite regardless of the fact that resistance had long since ceased.

A bookmaker, arm broken, head gashed in several places, tried to escape down the hill; but a man armed with a hammer was gaining with every step. The bookmaker gave a terrified look back over his shoulder and recognised his pursuer. He cried out, "You've made a bloomer! We are Leeds men."

The man with the hammer lowered his arm. "My God, I hope not," he said. "Anyway, get into the field and hide behind the trees. Or else they'll kill you. There's no stopping them now."

The near massacre was ended by the sound of approaching Flying Squad cars, bells ringing. The Birmingham Boys jumped into their coach and fled. The police would normally have given immediate chase. But with the roadside and the field beyond looking like a battleground, they decided to tend the injured until the ambulances arrived.

There wasn't a single man on the lorry who emerged unscathed. Most of them were suffering from fractures, while their wounds were so deep and the blood loss so severe that it was a miracle no one died.

The Birmingham Boys had initially been puzzled by the absence of Darby and the top Sabini soldiers. It was only when the hammer-wielder recounted the words of the Leeds bookmaker that the truth dawned. The men they had wounded so terribly were not their intended victims, the Sabinis, but members of the friendly Leeds Mob.

They drove somewhat rashly to the George and Dragon public house in Kingston and walked into the saloon bar ... their hands and clothing bearing the stains of their victims' blood.

The police had already put out a description of the coach and it was soon spotted by a village bobby. Within minutes the pub was surrounded by Flying Squad officers. Twenty-eight of the Birmingham Boys were arrested and twenty-three of them were jailed.

Later that evening the Sabinis celebrated in the Griffin. Big Tex shared the pride of place at the bar with Darby ... and no one needed to be told that their feud at Epsom had been skilfully staged.

Tex took a rotor arm out of his pocket, considered it seriously and said, "What do you reckon we should do with this ... send it back to them?"

Darby was laughing. "I think we should," he said. "After all, we're honest men."

When George Sewell awoke, it was late. He could tell by the sun coming in through the drawn blinds. It never came in that way unless it was the afternoon. There was a dull throb in his temples, a reminder of a tour of the clubs that had only ended with the dawn. He climbed instantly out of bed, slipped on the plain silk dressing gown that he used to wear in the ring, and walked into the kitchen. His wife Hetty must have had everything ready, hot in the oven, the tray waiting to be loaded, because as he lit the first cigarette of the day she placed it all upon the table. She was tall, fair-haired, attractive, a strongly-built woman.

"Joey Abrahams called," she said. "He says he's expecting trouble tonight at the Blue Moon. Wants to know if you'll go round and sort it out. I told him you would."

He grimaced. "Maybe I should send you instead. The kind of trouble Joey gets you could handle without even trying." He started to smile, felt the warning ache in his head, and changed his mind.

Before their marriage, women friends had expressed concern for her safety. But during the years they'd spent together, he had never once given her cause to fear him. Other women she'd known had suffered beatings from their husbands and accepted them as a matter of course. But he had never laid violent hands upon her or even threatened to do so.

After a quarrel he would become at worst coldly polite. But for much of the time he was a surprisingly warm-hearted and romantic lover. He was like many men who show a stone face to the world: his home in Peabody Buildings just behind the London Coliseum had become a much-needed refuge. The one place where he could totally relax and release the pent-up emotions.

He couldn't change overnight the habits of a lifetime, but he tried after his fashion. Hetty, a girl who had seen very little greenery in the city streets, had developed a passionate love of flowers. So whenever Georgie was on a night-long jaunt he would make a point of visiting nearby Covent Garden and taking home some spring flowers with which to surprise her. It was always the spring flowers she liked the best.

In the early days of her marriage she had been surprised by the degree of fear this husband of hers could put into the hearts of other men. She would overhear people discussing the Cobblestone Fighter guardedly and it was as though they were talking about someone she'd never known. In her youth and innocence, she convinced herself that these people had fashioned a legend merely to colour the reality.

Then one night in a bar, a big and arrogant man had spilt his drink down her dress and put laughter where an apology should have been. He was still laughing when the first blow landed, and within seconds he had been reduced to a broken and bloody hulk upon the floor. By no stretch of the imagination could this have been described as a fight. The man had simply been overwhelmed by a primeval force of nature.

Hetty had been raised in Hoxton, a tough part of the city, and so had witnessed her fair share of violence; but she had never seen anything quite like this before. Nor was it just the speed and suddenness of that attack which stayed in her mind. Above all else it had been the look of murderous fury on the face of the man she loved. For the first time she had glimpsed the darker side of his nature.

She watched him getting dressed. He was always fastidiously neat. She could see him frowning because the shirt he had put on wasn't laundered to his taste; the cuff links, a pair he hadn't worn for some time, were a little too loud for

51

the way he liked to dress now. She laughed softly and said, "Joey won't notice the difference."

"Not with all that big, bad trouble he's having," he said.

She knew he was depressed and understood him well enough to know the reason why.

"Will Darby have been all right on the Downs? she asked.

"If trouble came, he would have been alone," he said. "Those impostors who follow him around would make a point of being some place else."

"You've always liked Darby," she said. "Why didn't you go with him?"

"He never asked me," replied the Cobblestone Fighter.

6

HARRYBOY'S SOLUTION

"These gangs must be smashed and they will be"
— Sir William Joynson-Hicks,
the Home Secretary.

Sir William Joynson-Hicks, the Home Secretary, was standing at the Dispatch Box in the House of Commons surveying the packed benches with a satisfied eye. One of the great orators of his day, Jix, as he was affectionately known, liked to have an audience and today he was in full flow.

"The honourable gentleman is quite correct," he was saying. "The racecourse gangs have become a national disgrace. Not content with besmirching England's good name on the turf — a name renowned around the globe for fair play — they have now brought their thuggery on to the streets of our cities, wounding and maiming innocent passers-by. You can rest assured that I will do everything in my power to put a stop to this. These gangs must be smashed and they will be. Only remember, it may take a little time. I have asked our excellent police forces nationwide to send me a report on race gangs in their area. And we are considering the setting up of a special squad to combat this evil in our midst."

The statement may have been a little flowery — Jix's statements often were — but it nevertheless received the full support of the House. For everyone liked Jix. He was so patently honest and filled with good intentions. There was just one trouble with him. It seems doubtful whether Britain ever had a Home Secretary less streetwise than Jix.

He just couldn't understand why other people didn't wish to abide by his own high standards. And the current wave of street warfare horrified him.

The race gangs had simply chosen new battlegrounds. Whereas previously their wars had been waged on the courses and on race trains, they were now battling openly on the streets. Motorised cavalcades of armed men were carrying out lightning raids on rival headquarters.

In Aldgate, a razor battle involving fifty thugs was broken up by baton-wielding police.

At Victoria Station, a small army of racing men and women attacked Police Constable William Gatford and threw his unconscious body on to the lines.

And in Mornington Crescent, some Birmingham gang members and their wives were fired upon by a band of Sabinis. Darby shook his head sadly at the news. "I never thought the day would come," he said, "when I'd be told we were making war on women. After all, we're not hooligans."

But, ironically, the event which finally stirred Jix into action was the mythical Battle of Petticoat Lane, something dreamed up by the newspapers of the day. According to the reports, fifty mobsters armed with razors had fought one another between the market stalls in broad daylight, stopping the traffic and terrifying the citizens.

What really happened was that a bookmaker had been set upon and slashed by six members of the Bethnal Green Gang, close allies of the Hoxton Mob, on a Whitechapel street corner. This was the result of an argument that had begun earlier that day at Lewes Races.

It was midnight in Little Italy and the heat of the day lingered on. A breathless heat that was slowly driving the world mad. The most virtuous matrons found themselves looking at strangers with wild, wanton eyes. And mild little men fought down the desire to bay at the moon.

Harryboy, who could never have been described as mild, was standing outside the Griffin reflecting upon the injustices of life. The Sabinis had been steadily fashioning their criminal empire. They were already the major force upon the southern racecourses. Little Italy was now considered impregnable, and large areas of clubland were paying their dues into the gang's coffers. But Harryboy was still a long way from the hub of power.

Darby had made it clear that he valued him as a soldier in the regime, a breaker of heads; but that he was still too immature, too rash, too impulsive to be regarded as a leader of men. For months Harryboy had been trying to think of a way in which he could change that opinion, some dramatic act of valour that would force Darby's hand. And it was at that moment, as the clock of St Peter's chimed out midnight, that a taxi stopped outside the Gray's Inn police station and Georgie Sewell alighted.

To Harryboy it all seemed like the answer to a prayer, some message from above. Sewell was the one man in London who truly threatened the rise of the Sabinis. Whenever they met in the pubs and clubs frequented by the underworld, he displayed a thinly-veiled contempt for this band of Italians who had now moved into the major leagues.

In the past two years, he had spanked half a dozen of Harryboy's faction, cutting them down to size with brutal efficiency. In the world of gangland, where respect was essential for survival, such acts were normally regarded as a challenge that had to be answered. But Darby had always been reluctant to make a move against this legendary hard man. He had even counselled some of the firebrands in the band to step quietly around him. However, supposing Harryboy could now wipe out this threat to the mob, succeed at the task from which his brother had seemingly shied away? After such a feat, he would surely be the idol of Little Italy.

As Sewell began to walk towards the coffee stall in front of the Griffin, Harryboy faded back into the darkness. He noted that Sewell was accompanied by two pro fighters, Joe Davis and Joe Bloomfield; but at this time of night the hot streets were lined with Sabini soldiers. Harryboy moved amongst them, picking his team.

Meanwhile the three men sipped their coffee, unaware of the band waiting there in the darkness. Bloomfield, by nature a peaceful man, said, "This place has begun to give me the creeps. Don't you ever get nervous down here at night, George?"

The Cobblestone Fighter smiled by way of reply. "I was raised in these streets," he said simply. "You don't really think I'd let a bunch of Raddies drive me out, do you?"

A few minutes later Bloomfield put down his cup, bade his friends goodnight and went home. Davis was called to speak to a man on the other side of the road. Only then did Harryboy, eight-handed, launch the attack.

Before he could turn Sewell was struck over the back of the head with an iron bar. The blow, powerful enough to have crushed the average skull, rendered him dazed and helpless. A knuckleduster pulped his nose, razors slashed at his face and body. Pride and a savage anger kept him on his feet until he finally fell unconscious into the gutter. Even then they continued to kick him viciously.

In the end it was the spreading pool of blood which caused them to run away from the Clerkenwell Road. They had left him for dead, and Harryboy was already wondering whether he would have to pay for this night's work with his own life.

But before their running footsteps could fade into the night, Sewell had incredibly regained consciousness and risen to his knees, his face a mask of hatred.

Darby welcomed Billy Kimber politely to his home, but without any display of warmth. He seated him at a table laid in the Italian tradition ... a freshly baked loaf, great chunks of cheese and a carafe of anisette, a liquorice-flavoured wine. As a concession to Kimber's essential Englishness, there were also six bottles of beer.

Kimber, that man of refined taste, chose the wine. He had come on a mission of peace proposed by the bookmakers' spokesman Walter Beresford, the William Hill of his day. He sipped the wine, commenting, "Raw, but interesting."

However, Darby was in no mood for pleasantries. "Walter tells me you want to make the peace. And I agree it's time we stopped this nonsense. It can only harm our business interests, so tell me what you have in mind."

Kimber was one of the few gang leaders who spoke as quietly and as reasonably as Darby. He now embarked upon what was clearly a prepared speech:

"Before the Italians became involved, we had peace on the racecourse. There were no beatings, no razors, no hammers. Now none of us dare step on to a track unless we're carrying arms. It is more than our life is worth. Every meeting has its incidents. Faces are slashed, men are beaten and kicked. They talk about us in parliament, call us thugs who bring shame on the nation, the lowest of the low. Soon there will be no business for any of us. We will be barred from all the courses; and then how will we survive?"

He paused, inviting Darby to speak. But instead the Italian rose and filled Kimber's glass. He had spotted a tell-tale bulge in his visitor's powder-blue suit and, from his standing position, his suspicions were confirmed. Kimber had come to talk peace with a gun in his pocket.

Darby gave no sign that he knew. Once seated again, he simply said, "Walter tells me you have terms …"

Kimber wasn't to be hurried. "You have to understand," he said, "that today I don't merely act as a spokesman for Birmingham. I also speak for Leeds, Uttoxeter and Hoxton. These are hard, often violent, men who don't always understand you the way I do. Their wish is to drive every Italian out of racing, make it the way it was before. But I am not that greedy. There is after all room for everybody just so long as we all behave as reasonable men." Again he paused.

Darby sighed. "So just what are these terms of yours?" he asked.

"Keep your men away from Epsom and Ascot," Kimber replied flatly. "After all, these have belonged to us for many years. Then if you agree to that, we can come to some agreement about the other southern courses, let you have an agreed number of pitches on each. Then there would be no more talk of war and we could all profit."

The suggestion might have sounded reasonable to an outsider. But Epsom and Ascot were the two great money courses, the flagships for gangland empires; for whoever controlled these effectively controlled racing.

Darby chose to be oblique. "How about the bookmakers?" he asked. "Before we came into the game they were paying you for their pitches, sums so high that they were being put out of business. Those who dared to stand against you carried their scars to the grave. Now they hire their pitches from us at half the price and we protect them. The only fear they have is of you."

This was of course the reason why Beresford had been so anxious to arrange a truce. The war had placed bookmakers in an impossible position. If they paid their pitch money to one gang, they would immediately arouse the hostility of the others.

Kimber spoke dismissively. "The bookmakers you protect have one thing in common. They are all Jewish." He spread his hands wide, the gesture of an understanding man. "Of course, I don't share these prejudices. But my men are English and they don't take kindly to foreign ways. The Jews may have settled here, but they will never be accepted. This is England and yet we have a position on the racetracks where Jews are being protected by Italians. It is an impossible situation. If it continues all the other factions will combine against you. That's why I've come as a peaceful man to offer you a way out."

Darby smiled, but only with his lips. "You take a very moral tone," he said, "for a man who set out to murder us only a few weeks ago."

"Murder?" queried Kimber, looking suitably surprised. "No one died at Ewell. A little blood was shed. There were sore heads, but nothing more."

Darby didn't deign to quibble. Instead he said, "I like to

believe you came here today in good faith. But you've merely offered me something I already have. We already operate on the park courses. Brighton belongs to us, so do Bath and Lewes.

"As for this talk of Epsom and Ascot, I can only imagine that someone less sensible than yourself put that thought in your mind. They belong to whoever is strong enough to take them and to hold them. They are already ours."

Kimber was about to interrupt, but Darby raised an imperious hand. He was changing visibly, becoming the warlord that he really was. "You talk of terms," he said. "I'll tell you mine. The South belongs to us. It is after all our province. We're southern men. If your people forsake their warlike ways, we'll allow them to wet their beaks, but that's all. And in return we'll pledge to stay away from the Midlands and the North. That belongs to you. Those are my terms. You can either choose to accept them or it's war, and we have barely begun."

Billy Kimber was changing too, and suddenly all the gutter toughness was showing through. "You Guinea bastard!" he shouted. "You'll have every man's hand against you." He paused. "I'm looking at a dead man."

Darby smiled quite equably, and it was this smile that persuaded the man from Birmingham to commit a foolish act. He rose and reached for his gun.

In the ring Darby had always been noted for the speed of his hands, and that speed served him well now. He pulled out that big, flat gun of his and shot his rival. Kimber's own hand hadn't even reached his gun butt. The force of the bullet drove Kimber backwards, toppling the chair and sending him sliding across the floor. Kimber groaned once and then lay still. Even during the reflex action of firing Darby had been careful to aim for a non-lethal part of the human body, the upper thigh.

There was the sound of running feet on the pavement outside followed by a pounding on the door. Darby opened to see the concerned face of Nino, who had been standing guard at the far end of the street.

Darby took Kimber's gun and fired it through the open window into the night sky. The denizens of Little Italy had long since learned the wisdom of hearing and seeing nothing.

They carried Kimber through the dark streets, finally leaving him on the pavement with his back propped against a wall. They left the recently fired gun beside him and then put an anonymous call through to the police.

Later that same evening Alfie Solomons went to the Cray's Inn Road police station and confessed to having shot Billy Kimber in self-defence. But Kimber, true to the gangland code, was unable to help the authorities. He'd been shot, he said, by a complete stranger; and that stranger certainly wasn't Alfie Solomons.

The Houses of Parliament were little more than a mile as the crow flies from Little Italy. Yet until the coming of the racecourse wars, Jix had barely known of that district's existence. But as the reports from the various police chiefs poured into the Home Office, the names of Darby Sabini and the Italian Mob assumed a greater significance day by day. So eventually he decided out of curiosity to pay a private visit to this area of the city that appeared to have been taken over by a foreign army.

He went by night, and was pleasantly surprised to find a friendliness on the streets that was missing from other areas of London. He visited the Unione Roma Club in Little Bath Street and was again impressed by the welcoming smiles. It was only when he came to pay for his meal that the troubles came. His wallet was missing. All of a sudden the waiter had stopped smiling and so had the manager.

At this point, a barrel-chested man who had been following these exchanges with interest turned to the manager and said, "This is clearly a stranger in trouble, so I will gladly settle his account."

Jix hastened to explain that his wallet must have been stolen; but his new-found friend would have none of this. "No one steals anything in Little Italy," he said. "These are law-abiding people. Poor but honest. Tell me the streets you walked along and I am sure we will recover your wallet in no time at all."

The man talked earnestly to some men he'd been dining with and they left hurriedly. Sure enough within ten minutes they'd returned with the wallet, notes intact. Jix wanted to reward this Good Samaritan, but the barrel-chested man refused. So Jix said, "At least, tell me your name."

The man hestitated for a brief moment. "Charles," he said. "Charles Sabini."

Jix paused in turn. "No relation, I suppose, to Darby Sabini?"

"Heaven forbid," said the man and smiled his golden smile. In later years Darby was fond of recounting this tale. "Just imagine," he'd say, "a Home Secretary having his pocket picked … a man in charge of the law of a nation being green enough to let Boffa pick his pocket. I ask you. What's the country coming to?"

7

THE BRIGHTON AFFAIR

"You know, I don't really like Italians" —
Georgie Sewell, speaking to Darby Sabini.

All day long, hard-faced men had been arriving at the Horns public house in Shoreditch. Many of them had accents which puzzled the locals, but no one cared to comment upon that fact. There are times in life when it can be wise to remain silent, and this was one of them. They were witnessing the most formidable array of gangland talent ever assembled under one banner. Mobsters from Wales, Birmingham, Manchester and Sheffield were linking forces with the London gangs for a monumental showdown with the Sabinis.

The attack on Georgie Sewell had prompted the alliance, and on the morrow, Whit Monday, they would raid the Brighton racecourse. The plan was simple enough. Sewell would fight Harryboy, and under cover of this disturbance, the other gangs would finish off the hated Italians once and for all.

Since the midnight attack outside the Griffin, the Cobblestone Fighter had seemingly disappeared as if off the face of the earth. The underworld, always a hotbed of gossip, boiled with speculation.

Many, including Harryboy, were convinced that Georgie had died from his wounds. Others believed that the iron man had been beaten at last, and that realising the impossibility of taking on a mob single-handed, he'd fled the city.

The truth was stranger than that. He'd had his face stitched together by a gangland doctor and even as the sutures had been going in, he'd been planning his revenge. He had left the doctor's rooms on remarkably steady feet and taken a cab to his flat in Peabody Buildings.

It was then that Jack Watts, a fairground showman and gang leader from the East End with a particular hatred of the Sabinis, had taken a hand in the game. Realising that Sewell, as a freelance enforcer, was maybe the one man in the land who could be used to unite the rival factions, he made him an offer. If Sewell would promise to stay out of sight for a few weeks, thus lulling the Sabinis into a false sense of security, Watts would hand him Harryboy on the proverbial plate. A fight to the finish between the two of them with the guarantee that no other Sabini would be allowed to intervene.

Sewell had agreed instantly. There was nothing in the world he wanted more than a few minutes alone with Harryboy.

He had always been a quick healer, and as soon as the stitches had been removed, he began training for the battle to come in a room above Watts's gambling club in Mansell Street, Aldgate. There were bare-knuckle sessions with Joe Davis and Joe Bloomfield, no time called and no quarter given.

As the mobsters gathered in the bar of the Horns, Sewell had been sleeping in a room above. And now Watts, like the showman he was, invited him down into the bar.

Then in his barker's voice he shouted out, "There you are, boys. That's what those Raddies did to one of our pals."

The bar went silent as they turned to look at the Cobblestone Fighter, who was standing on the bottom landing. Razor slashings were part and parcel of these men's lives, and yet even so a buzz went up at the sight of those red and angry scars on the face of the enforcer. Under the bright light of the landing they looked particularly grotesque.

But it wasn't just the scars they were studying. They had heard rumours too of the hunter who had been finally tamed; and as this was the man fronting the raid, they needed to be sure it wasn't so.

Watts held out his arms in a fatherly gesture. "Tell me once again, Georgie, will you fight Harryboy at Brighton?"

Sewell shrugged. "What kind of damn fool question is that?" he asked.

He smiled, and the freshly scarred face made that smile appear more cold, more chilling, than anything even he could have imagined.

It was Sam Garvin, the Sheffield mob leader, who broke the silence. "A broken man?" he asked. "God help Harryboy!" Laughter rumbled down the length of the bar.

Bank Holiday crowds poured into Brighton. People stood packed deep on the buses that took them out to the Kemp Town track. Overloaded taxis groaned up the steep hill towards the racecourse. And Darby stood there in the sunshine, at peace with his world, totally unaware of the avenging army that was coming to destroy him. Just for once his intelligence service had failed him, and at a time when he needed it most.

By some ill chance he had taken a fortnight's holiday prior to the meeting and his informers, unable to reach him, had refused to talk to anyone else. With this awesome alliance, the risk of discovery was too terrifying to contemplate. Darby, with his marvellous antennae, might well have anticipated this move if he had known of the attack on Georgie Sewell. But Harryboy had buried that secret deep, still fearful of the hangman's rope.

Finally it was his long-time friend, Bernie the bookmaker, who gave him the unwelcome news.

"You'll have to run, Darby," he said, "and so will I. The mobs are coming."

For the moment Darby didn't take him too seriously. "What, *all* the mobs, Bernie?" he asked.

"Yes, Darby, *all* the mobs," said Bernie flatly. "The northern mobs have banded together with the London gangs. Over four hundred armed men are on the way. Lorry-loads of them with Georgie Sewell at their head."

A strange look came into the eyes of Darby. He'd dreamed of moments such as this, and in the worst of the nightmares it had always been the face of Georgie Sewell that he'd seen in the flicker of a second before he'd woken. Then the spectre passed and he was his calm, confident self again. He didn't bother asking Bernie whether he was sure. He just said, "Thanks, Bernie, you go with my people. Don't worry about picking up your things from the pitch. I'll take care of that."

Within seconds the bush telegraph was transmitting its message around the course, and the Sabinis were on their way. It was as though the earth had swallowed them up. Darby made no attempt to follow them and nor did Harryboy who, having been absent from his pitch when the message arrived, was still blissfully unaware of the approaching danger.

From his position on the hill, Darby spotted the cavalcade of lorries and limousines when they were still half a mile from the course. It was unusual to see seven lorries in a row, but it wasn't this that tipped him. It was the sight of Georgie Sewell's powder-blue Buick leading the way that confirmed his worst fears.

There was no question that the violence in Georgie Sewell's nature rose from some deep, mysterious well. As he spotted Harryboy at his bookmaking joint chalking up the odds for the first race, his eyes filled with hatred. He stood there for a moment, stunned by his own rage. At that instant he was capable of anything. Then he said to the mob around him, "Remember he's mine. No matter what happens, no one gets in the way. Otherwise I'll have them too."

When Harryboy first saw the Cobblestone Fighter he thought he'd seen a ghost. He had so convinced himself that the man was dead that he was unable to readjust.

The sight of Sewell hurtling towards him, his face a mask of fury, only added to the shock. Sewell hooked him twice to the head, two stunning blows; and before Harryboy could fall, Sewell grabbed him by the throat, determined to drag him away from the shelter of the joint.

But Harryboy wrapped his huge muscular arms around a post and hung on. His shirt ripped away in Sewell's hands and what followed was sickening. Sewell proceeded to beat the cowering Harryboy with his fists, cursing him in a thick, rage-choked voice. Harryboy, despite his own impressive physique, offered no resistance, gave no cry for mercy or protest. It wasn't that he was a coward in the normal sense of the word, merely that he had convinced himself that he had no chance at all when opposed to the savage power of this man.

Sewell's fellow-mobsters had formed a ring around them which no one dared to break. And in the end it was Harryboy's refusal to fight back that saved his life. The paradox in Sewell's violent nature was that he couldn't hit a woman and had never done so. Nor could he harm a child or anything helpless. And finally Harryboy's complete submission rendered him harmless too. It disarmed the Cobblestone Fighter's violence, and with one last curse he walked away.

While this had been happening the gangs had taken over the course and collected the pitch money. But like Sewell himself, they were frustrated by the lack of opposition. They had come prepared for war and found no one to fight.

So when Darby was spotted near Tattersalls they saw the opportunity to turn the day once more to their advantage. Darby, quickly surrounded, was edged towards the enclosure rails. He was alone and patently unafraid. They hoped he would try to run so that they could slash him across the legs with their razors and bayonets and bring him down. But Darby stood there smiling, his hand inside his jacket resting on his gun.

"Well, boys, what's this all about?" he asked.

And Sewell, pushing his way through the crowd, pointed to the scars on his face and said, "That's Harryboy's work. Now I've settled that score, but my pals here are after you, Darby, and the rest of your lot."

"Not now, Georgie," said Darby matter-of-factly, as though discussing some business deal. "Outsiders might get hurt. But I'll meet your boys, just as many as you like, at the Russell when racing is over, and that's a promise."

"What time?" asked Sewell, a man who lived his life upon the ticking of a clock.

"Eight, or maybe five minutes either way," said Darby; and the appointment having been made, the mobs drifted away.

Over two hundred and fifty gangsters packed the Russell that Bank Holiday evening. They crammed the saloon and public bars and spilled out on to the forecourt. The police seemed to be absent, though in the crush it was hard to tell. The mobsters had been drinking steadily all day, and as the witching hour of eight o'clock approached, their mood was murderous.

Although initially taken by surprise on the course, Darby had reacted brilliantly. By getting his men to fade away like a ghost army, he had avoided certain and bloody defeat, while buying himself the time to think. But even so it was hard to see how either Darby or the Sabinis could survive until nightfall.

They had seemingly two stark choices. They could either come mob-handed, in which case they would be overwhelmed by the sheer weight of numbers, either killed or maimed. Or they could fail to appear, which was possibly even worse. Under the rigid code by which gangland operated they would be branded as impostors. The Sabini empire-building would be finished, and once more Little Italy would become the happy hunting ground for rival gangs.

As eight o'clock chimed out from the Town Hall clock, the noise in the bar was deafening, the air taut with anticipation. There was as yet no sign of the Sabinis, but Darby had said five minutes either way and he was a man who made a habit of keeping his word.

And then at five minutes past eight precisely, the door of the saloon bar swung open and Darby stood framed in the doorway. He had a white and blue cap on his head and a freshly lit cigarette in his mouth. A diamond pin blinked from his choker. He had clearly dressed for the occasion. He was completely alone, no other Sabini in sight.

Abruptly the saloon fell silent and the noise from other bars magically dwindled away. Darby began to move towards Georgie Sewell, who was standing in the place of honour at the centre of the bar. Darby was as near to being a dead man as it's possible to be and he must have known that, and yet nothing showed in that peasant face of his. Men stepped aside to let the Italian through. There was something almost inhuman about the confidence of the man.

The silence was so intense that when Darby put his hand on Sewell's shoulder and in his quiet voice said, "Come on, Georgie, let's have a drink. Haven't we always been pals?" the words boomed around the Russell like a railway announcement.

He pulled out a wallet fat with fivers, handed three to a barmaid and ordered, "Drinks for all my pals. Drinks for everybody." Then turning once more towards the Cobblestone Fighter, he said, "Come on, Georgie, what's it going to be?"

Still the spell didn't break and, at that moment, Sewell had the gang leader's life in the palm of his hand. All he had to do was refuse the proffered drink and Darby would have been down on the floor, being stomped to death by countless anonymous feet.

But with his uncanny gift for survival, Darby had had the good fortune to have picked a man who prized gameness above all other human virtues. After what must have seemed an eternity Sewell said, "Make it a double," and the deadly spell had been broken at last.

The barmaid bustled forward with the first of the orders and Darby, timing as immaculate as ever, withdrew a wad of notes and began handing them out to eager tearaways clustered around the bar. He was beyond harm. No one in that violent company would have dared touch him now.

He spent half an hour chatting with the men who had come to destroy him. Before leaving he shook Sewell's hand and said in that quiet voice of his, "I'll be seeing you, Georgie."

Again the ranks parted. He moved jauntily towards the door and no one made a move to stop him. He had saved the Sabinis the only way he knew how.

In the days that followed, gangland carried out its own form of accounting for what had become known as the Brighton Affair. It was generally agreed that among the Sabinis only Darby had come out of this with any credit.

The majority of his followers were still regarded as impostors, and there were some isolated cases of Sabini Boys being spanked around the clubs.

But it was part of the greatness of Darby that he could always find a way to profit from every disaster, and this was to be no exception. Two weeks to the day since their last meeting in the Russell, Darby and Georgie Sewell met again, this time in the Blue Moon and at Darby's invitation. Darby ordered a bottle of brandy and a bottle of champagne and immediately came to the heart of the matter.

"I know you like working alone, Georgie," he said, "but I need you. Come with me and I'll give you the sort of deal you've dreamed about."

Sewell looked into his eyes. "You know," he said, "I don't really care for Italians."

Darby smiled slightly. "Tell you the truth, I don't either. That's why I need you. You'd be my right hand. I want someone there I can trust completely. It would be just you and me. You wouldn't be expected to mix with the rest of the mob. Just tell me what you want and it will be yours. I know that if we work together nothing can stop us. So what do you say, Georgie, are you with me?"

The Cobblestone Fighter had been asked that question many times by other men, and always the answer had been 'No'.

He had an oceanic disrespect for the talents of other gangsters and he'd never had a hero. Yet he still had that vision of Darby in the Russell. Calm and smiling, yet knowing his life was in the balance. He had never seen a braver or a cleverer man, or one he admired more.

But he didn't say any of that. He just shrugged and said casually enough, "I'll give it a try."

Darby reached out and shook his hand: a curiously English gesture for a man who, despite his protestations to the contrary, was at heart a Mafia Don.

8

THE DISAPPEARING GUN

*"They are outside now. I don't think there's
anywhere left to run"* — *warning for
Darby Sabini at Epsom.*

It was Derby Day 1922 and the world and his wife were
heading for Epsom Downs. Charabancs nudged bumpers
with lordly Daimlers. And Darby sat alone behind the glass
partition of his chauffeur-driven Austin de luxe, wondering
whether this was to be his last day on earth. He had been
warned that should he arrive on the racecourse, the Birmingham Boys would make an attempt on his life; and that
prospect didn't alarm him as much as it might have done a
more normal man in a more normal line of work.

Ever since his accession to the kingship of Little Italy, he
had accepted the probability that he would never make old
bones. Many of the British gangs were led by men who were
little more than figureheads. But the Sabinis had fashioned
themselves upon the Mafia of Sicily, where the head of the
family was supreme in his power. The fortunes of the
Sabinis would rest upon the cunning, the craft, the courage
and quite possibly the cruelty of their leader. If that leader
should die in the full flush of manhood, then the Sabinis
would virtually die too. There was no natural successor
within the ranks. So Darby had become a very special target
for his enemies in general, and for the Birmingham Boys in
particular.

Racing had become the true love of Darby's life. He
found a certain fascination in boxing, and he took pleasure

from the clubs of Little Italy. But for him there was a magic in the turf that he could find no place else. He didn't know much about horses, apart from what he could glean from the form book; but he regarded the great ones with awe and, despite the odds, hated to see them beaten. The pint-sized jockeys with weatherbeaten faces and hands of silk were the only idols he'd ever known. Yet even this love for the game hadn't been enough on its own account to prompt him into making this challenge to the established racecourse gangs.

He had simply looked upon it as the logical extension of his plans. Already he was dreaming dreams so grandiose that they would have staggered even his wildest admirers, and for that reason he kept them to himself. He had decided to become the supreme power in the British underworld, and this had been one more carefully considered step along the way. The most important step so far.

He was travelling as part of a Sabini cavalcade. Up in front he could see the Bugatti of Massarda followed by a Buick, a Humber, a grey Chrysler. Bringing up the rear was a lorry loaded with bookmaking stands, young Italians and liquid refreshment. Despite that show of strength, he took the most comfort from the big gun tucked into the waistband of his trousers.

He had no illusions about his own vulnerability during the long day that lay ahead. There would be over half a million people out there on the Downs, and their numbers only added to his personal danger. The attack could come from anywhere at any time; and the would-be assassins could slip away so easily in that huge crowd. A bullet or a deftly wielded knife could put a sudden and final seal upon his dreams.

Despite the heat of the day, he wore the check-cap, black muffler and dark attire that had become his trademark. And as the grandstand and downs loomed up in the distance, he remembered something his grandfather had said on a similar occasion many years ago. "A good day for dying," he'd said. It was a sentiment that Darby had never shared. He couldn't believe that there could ever be a good day upon which to wave the world goodbye.

Detective Inspector William Rawlings was a worried man. From the control room in the roof of the grandstand, he was looking out over a sea of faces, paradise for the pickpockets and the con men. With no more than a dozen men at his command, he knew that the task of combatting that particular brand of villainy was a hopeless one. So he had concentrated his entire attention upon the organised gangs because they at least operated in a compact area, namely around the bookmakers' ring.

For years he had managed to keep a precarious peace by allowing one gang to control the pitches on each course. It was a practical solution to the problem rather than an ethical one. But now all his schemes had been put at risk by the impending arrival of the Sabinis on a course that had for so long been regarded as the natural stamping ground for the Birmingham boys. Unless he could conjure up the wisdom of a Solomon, there would be open warfare on this, the most famous day in the racing calendar; and this was the part of the job that he hated. It involved a compromise that smacked of corruption. It meant turning a Nelson-like eye towards the activities of the Birmingham mobsters, so that to the public at large the scene would seem as peaceful as before.

Rawlings had always been an honest cop, and a brave one. He had spent years on the beat. Soon the young toughs who'd been terrorising the streets began to flee at the very sight of him. He had been a very tough cop and a very fair one. He gave the shopkeepers a lot of protection, a lot of service. He would help the old and the infirm across the busy streets. When some of the neighbourhood kids threatened to run wild, he straightened them out with a cuff around the ear. He had a heavy hand and seldom needed to perform that service twice. He spent many of his off-duty hours at a boys' club, teaching them to box, to grow up as good citizens instead of hoodlums.

He was a man who'd loved his work and he played it all by the book. In the end he played it too well. When a wine store was held up at gunpoint, he heard the screams and, brave as a bull, charged through the door. He took a bullet through the upper arm, but still took the gun away from the man and left him unconscious upon the floor. By the time Rawlings came out of hospital, he'd been transferred to the detective branch.

It was the worst thing that ever happened to him. He was no longer the friend of honest men and women, no longer the fatherly neighbourhood cop. To his chagrin, he soon discovered that many detectives are only a shade more honest than the men they pursue; and that even the most trustworthy believe in the system of what they term 'clean graft'. So reluctantly, he'd allowed himself to be carried along by the tide. He had risen rapidly through the ranks, been showered with commendations, and soon he would be a superintendent. But he often wished he was back on the beat, and never more so than today.

He had already decided that for the general good Darby's life had to be put at risk. His men down on the gates had instructions to search the gold-toothed Italian upon arrival and take away the big gun that he reputedly carried upon his person at all times. In the previous summer, Darby had drawn and fired that gun on the Greenford racecourse ... and the possibility of such a thing happening on Derby Day just couldn't be considered.

Rawlings knew that this meant leaving Darby virtually defenceless against the armed savagery of the Birmingham Boys. But he consoled his conscience with the thought that the Italian was a gang leader who wouldn't be greatly missed by honest men. And if this was the only way in which gang warfare could be kept off the racecourses of England, then so be it.

He had never previously set eyes upon Darby, and it hadn't occurred to him for a single moment that the challenge of the Sabinis could prevail. As strangers in a strange land every hand would be against them, and it seemed to him a monumental piece of misjudgment.

A grizzled sergeant came into the room. "Sir, we picked

out Sabini. He came through the main gate."

"Did you take away the gun?"

"There was no gun, no weapon of any kind," replied the sergeant, and he smiled the way professionals do. "You can be sure of that. I searched him myself. If there had been so much as the smallest blade I'd have found it."

"Did he object?"

"Not at all," said the sergeant. "It was almost as though he was pleased to see me. He even offered to turn out his pockets."

Rawlings sensed the hesitation. "Anything else?" he asked.

The sergeant chuckled. "As a matter of fact there was something. When I'd finished with him, he advised me to put my money on Captain Cuttle in the big race. Said it was a good thing with Steve Donoghue riding."

Rawlings was intrigued. "What was your impression of him?"

"He seemed a likeable enough chap," said the sergeant. "But a bit out of his depth down here, a bit overawed by it all. Mark my word, he won't cause any trouble on the course today."

For the first time since he'd risen in the early dawn, Rawlings began to relax. And it was in that selfsame moment that the sound of gunfire carried across the downs.

Darby was drinking in a booth up on the hill, quiet and powerful, in the manner of a fellow anxious only to watch the world go by. And yet all the while his eyes were scanning the entrance, missing nothing. He had always believed that if a man wishes to be successful he must make a habit of trying to think the way an enemy might think. So long before he reached the course, he had reasoned that the police would come searching for his gun. To him, it seemed the logical move. So he'd handed the gun to Dai Thomas, a Welsh heavyweight who normally never carried a weapon of any kind, and was therefore unlikely to be searched. Now he was waiting for Thomas and the return of that gun.

He was still waiting when one of the young Italians, still

in his teens, came running into the booth to report that Bernie the Bookmaker, a known friend of the Sabinis, had just had his teeth kicked down his throat by a deputation of Birmingham Boys after having told them, "I'm going to pay the Raddies my pitch money today."

Darby noted almost absently that the boy's hand was shaking. He had been touched by a fear far greater than anything inspired by the story he'd just told.

"And what else is there," asked Darby, "that you find so hard to tell me?"

"They are looking for you too," said the boy. "They are outside now. I don't think there's anywhere left to run."

Darby felt the weakness in his legs, but none of this showed in his face.

"Well then, we mustn't run, must we?" he said.

The calmness of Darby sparked off a sudden resolve in the boy. "I'll stay with you," he said, hands still shaking. "I'll stand and fight for you."

Darby was touched. "No, it will be better if I go out there on my own and talk to the men," he said gently. "If trouble starts maybe you can slip away and get help. That way you would be doing me a service."

But he already knew that if there was a fight, help would be too slow in coming. The Birmingham Boys, old hands at this game, would complete their grim handiwork in a matter of seconds.

He contemplated the glass of whisky in his hand and poured it slowly and thoughtfully between the golden teeth. Then he went out into the sunshine to where his enemies were waiting. There were twelve in the brigade and they held the tools of their trade unabashedly in their hands. Some had pulled steel posts from the enclosure fences. Others had iron staves and bludgeons. One optimistically carried a Heath Robinson device, a hinged container worked on a Jack-in-the-box principle and holding a spring festooned with razor blades which he intended to aim at Darby. They formed a half-circle around him and moved in cautiously.

One quick glance had been enough to convince Darby

that he was cornered with the tent at his back and his enemies all around him; but the wariness of their approach held out a glimmer of hope. Clearly they hadn't realised that he was unarmed and therefore at their mercy. Otherwise there would have been a rush of feet and a quick ending to the affair. Realising that his life depended upon playing the bluff, Darby conjured up a smile of oceanic confidence and rested his hand just inside the coat flap on his right hip, the place where the gun would normally have been carried.

And all the while he was looking over the heads of his enemies, searching for Dai Thomas. Then at last he saw him. The Welshman was waving the gun frantically from the public enclosure.

Darby's response was instantaneous. Suddenly he sprinted into the very centre of the mob, roaring, holding that right hand close to the body. Afterwards several swore that they had seen the gun in his hand. Such are the powers of imagination.

Before they could recover from their surprise, he had crashed his way through their stunned ranks, reached Thomas, and snatched the gun from his hand. He turned and fired, and the bullet ploughed up the ground a yard ahead of the shuffling line of men. There could be no doubting the deadliness of his intent. He advanced two paces, took careful aim, squeezed the trigger and heard the dull click as the hammer descended on to a dud cartridge. He tried again and once more the cartridge let him down.

It didn't really matter, for the Birmingham Boys were already fleeing. Two policemen arrived and took the gun from Darby, who surrendered it with a smile, once more an affable man.

He made a token trip to the Epsom Town police station, but stayed barely ten minutes. As usual in such affairs, there were no witnesses. By the time he returned to the course Captain Cuttle had won the big race; and the Sabinis, encouraged by the ignominious flight of the Birmingham Boys, had collected the pitch money unopposed.

9

AT THE FRATALANZA

"You appear to be two lawless bands, the Sabinis and the Cortesis" — Mr Justice Darling, at the Old Bailey.

Harry Frenchie, the warlord of the Cortesis, was a man born out of his time. If he had remained in his native Sicily he would have been a brigand. And in Elizabethan days he would doubtless have sailed as a buccaneer. But in twentieth century London he would always look out of place, even on the streets of Little Italy. He was too wild, too vainglorious, for this city where commerce was the lifeblood.

He had once made his protest against the licensing laws by shooting at the bottles behind the bar in the Griffin as though they were targets in a fairground. Darby, amused by such eccentricity, had led the round of applause and paid for the damage.

But tonight that spirit of concord was nowhere to be seen. The Sabinis and their allies, the Cortesis, were on the brink of war. The cause of the dispute was the racecard with its list of runners which provided a considerable share of the Sabinis' income. The Cortesis had demanded to be cut in, and Darby had refused.

Now, as Darby walked along the Clerkenwell Road with Harry Frenchie on one side and Gus Cortesi on the other, he was watchful and wary.

"You can either be our friend," said Harry Frenchie, "or our enemy. The choice is yours. After all, there is plenty for everybody and all we wish to do is wet our beak."

Darby sighed. "You have both known me for many years. Haven't I always been a generous man? If your purse was empty and you came to me, I would fill it for you. If you have enemies, those enemies become my enemies. You know that this is so. But we are talking about something else. We are talking about my business and the business of men who trust me, a business we have created by the sweat of our brows. Tell me, would you go to a baker who was selling fine Italian pastries, ask him for half of his business and still talk of friendship?"

Harry Frenchie, who could never match Darby's fine flow of words, was growing angrier by the minute.

"Where would your business be without us?" he asked. "Haven't we always stood beside you? We are of the same race and yet you act as though we're strangers.

"Partners are supposed to share. But what have you ever shared with us apart from trouble? The Sabinis are becoming too big for their boots. We are the ones who pushed you up and we are the ones who can pull you down."

Darby shook his head as though sorely perplexed by this line of logic. "You speak of friendship and then in the same breath you speak of war. These are merely the words of anger and of weary men. Let's go home to our beds and meet again in the morning. By then I'm sure we'll be able to see reason."

Gus Cortesi spat on the pavement an inch from Darby's right boot by way of answer; but again it was Harry Frenchie who did the talking.

"Tell us now," he demanded, "are you going to let us wet our beaks?"

Darby shrugged, watching the two men even more closely than before. "You know my answer," he said.

For a moment it seemed as though the Cortesi warlord would hurl himself upon Darby. The anger within him was so fierce that his entire frame shook. Finally the shaking went away, but when the voice came it was half strangled by rage.

He said, "Then you give us no choice. We will kill you,

Darby Sabini."

The threat of immediate action was still there and yet Darby studied the two Cortesis, looking outwardly as calm as ever.

He smiled slightly. "Harry," he said, "you talk too much for a fighting man."

For Darby, this was to be a time of challenge. Another arrived the very next day in the rounded shape of Walter Beresford, who came knocking on Darby's door at what for this leader of the Sabinis was the ungodly hour of eleven o'clock in the morning.

Darby, bleary-eyed and unshaven, invited the bookmaker into what he liked to term the parlour. Beresford, normally the most confident of men, had a haunted look about him. Even his normally florid cheeks were drawn and pale. Darby poured a brandy without a word and noted that Beresford's hand was shaking as he took the glass.

"Trouble?" Sabini asked.

Beresford nodded fiercely. "Billy Kimber has barred all London bookmakers from the Leger. Told us to stay away from Doncaster."

"And if you don't?"

"We're dead men," replied Beresford.

Darby sipped his own drink thoughtfully. "Tell me," he said, "why have you come to me? You must know I have no interest in northern courses. I can protect you in the south, but Doncaster is no concern of mine. So although I would like to be of service, what can I do?"

"Couldn't you talk to Billy Kimber," suggested Beresford, "get him to change his mind? After all, if it hadn't been for your quarrel, we'd still have been welcome at the Leger."

"You mean," said Darby, ominously quiet, "that your present troubles are all of my making?"

Beresford refused to be intimidated, saying stubbornly, "Before you locked horns with Billy, we had an understanding with the Brummagem Mob. We were made welcome on all courses. None were barred to us."

Darby let the silence drag out. "Tell me," he said, "have

you ever feared me? Have you ever believed I would do you harm or run you out of business? Haven't I always been reasonable, demanding far less in pitch money than those hooligans in days gone by?"

Beresford nodded. But before he could say anything, Darby pressed on. "Yet you fear Billy Kimber; and because of that, you don't talk to him man to man. Instead you come and blame all your troubles on me. Is that really the way to treat a friend?"

While Darby had been talking, the bookmaker had been glancing around the room, noting the worn carpet, the shabby sofa, the galvanised tin bath hanging upon the wall. He wondered why a relatively wealthy man should wish to continue living in such a hovel. Over the years, many others would wonder that too.

Beresford shrugged. "You're right," he said. "It isn't your problem. It's just that we can't afford to be banned from the northern courses. I came to you for advice. So just tell us what to do."

"Stand and fight," said Darby simply. "Take a backward step and you'll never stop. If you want to go to Doncaster, go!"

"And if Billy Kimber carries out his threat?"

"He won't," said Darby positively. "I guarantee your safety."

And true to his word, he did. Beresford and a group of top London bookmakers arrived at King's Cross to discover that the Sabinis led by Darby had virtually taken over the train, searched every carriage and commandeered an entire coach. They travelled with the bookies, escorted them to the course and guarded them for the entire week. Gangsters from Sheffield, Leeds and Birmingham did a lot of prowling and glaring, but no one made an overtly hostile move. As Darby had rightly surmised, neither Billy Kimber nor Sam Garvey would wish to have had a racecourse battle staged on what they regarded as their own territory. With the Home Secretary already on the warpath, such an occurrence could have put them out of busines permanently.

Safely back at King's Cross, Beresford placed a hand on Darby's shoulder and stated in front of everyone, "Darby, you're a prince of a fellow. I just don't know how to thank you."

"You already have," said Darby. "You acted like a man."

But of course Darby's motives hadn't been prompted solely by a desire to help his fellow-man. By displaying the power to keep the London bookmakers free from harm, he had given the police pause for thought, while at the same time underlining his own kingship. The whole episode had served him well.

Louisa Doralli had matured into a striking beauty: perhaps a little too slim and feminine for the liking of some Mediterranean men, but sweet perfection in the eyes of Northern Europeans. She had a certain style too that lifted her out from the crowd, and it wasn't just by chance that Darby now spent as much time in the Fratalanza as he did in the Griffin.

With his strait-laced morality he was careful to keep the relationship on a strictly paternal basis; and it was true that he was immensely proud of her. The Doralli family had initially been the outcasts of this tightly-knit community, and for a strange reason. They spoke only Italian, a language which few of the exiles understood. Most of the inhabitants of Little Italy had been born in London and were anxious to blend into the life of the city. This was why, for instance, Pasquala Poppa chose to become known as Bert Marsh and why the Cortesi lieutenant, Alexander Tomaso, was named Sandy Rice. These were good old-fashioned English names.

But Enrico Doralli, proud of his Italian heritage, refused to adopt English ways. He remained aloof from his neighbours. Even worse, there were rumours that he was on friendly terms with the police. As a consequence his daughter Louisa, even though she came to speak fluent English, was cast into a lonely world. During her schooldays, there were no friends, no companions. The other children were simply obeying the dictates of their elders. Darby had sensed the unfairness of all this and named her as his goddaughter, making her an unofficial member of his own family, casting himself somewhat in the role of a favourite uncle.

He knew her life had been difficult and he appreciated the courage it had taken to rise above the prejudices of this intolerant society. But although he was reluctant to admit it to himself, there was a little more to his admiration than that of a father for a daughter. If he could have had his time again, this was the sort of woman he would have chosen. A strong woman who could look a man in the eye. A warm woman who put laughter into the heart. A beautiful woman who could be both friend and lover.

Hitherto he had spent most of his life in the company of men; but now he was never more content than when listening to his goddaughter. He wondered if maybe this was a sign he was growing old. She had just told him a joke, and he was laughing as he leaned against the bar. He was still laughing as five members of the Cortesi clan walked into the club.

Harry Frenchie (real name Enrico Cortesi) was flanked by his three brothers, Gus, Paul and George, and by Sandy Rice. They came in peacefully enough and asked for coffee.

"Sorry, I can't serve you," said Louisa, "this is a members-only club."

Then Gus Cortesi turned towards Darby, as though noticing him for the first time, and said, "Oh, here you are then, you … . This is the time to fight."

So saying, he drew a pistol from his hip pocket. But before he could use it, Louisa seized his hand and in the ensuing struggle, the gun fell to the floor.

Meanwhile Harry Frenchie had drawn his own gun and fired at Harryboy Sabini, wounding him in the right side of the abdomen. Harryboy tumbled slowly and lay unmoving on the boards.

Gus Cortesi, having regained his pistol, advanced upon Darby and took careful aim. Just for once in his life Darby was totally defenceless. There was nowhere to run and no way of warding off the bullet. But as Gus's finger tightened on the trigger, Louisa stepped in front of Darby, offering herself as a human shield.

"Stand aside," shouted Gus, a note of frenzy in his voice, "or I'll kill you too."

Darby, fearful for Louisa's life, thrust her aside. From a range of three yards, Gus fired and missed, the bullet passing harmlessly through the window.

Before he could fire again, his brothers Paul and George aided by Sandy Rice attacked Darby with bottles and became locked in close combat ... too close for Gus to risk firing again.

Darby's educated right hand connected with Sandy Rice's chin, sending him sliding over a table top before crashing into the wall.

Another woman had fallen on her knees beside Harryboy and turning a grief-stricken face towards the Cortesis screamed, "You bastards, you've killed him."

At this the Cortesis fled, convinced that they were leaving a dead man behind them. However, Harryboy, although seriously wounded and on the critical list, would survive the night's work. The bullet had passed straight through his abdomen and exited close to the spine. He was rushed still unconscious to the Royal Free Hospital in Gray's Inn Road; and after he'd gone Darby turned to Louisa.

"Didn't you know," he asked, "that a madman like that could have shot you down too?"

"Naturally I knew," said Louisa and continued to polish a glass as casually as though discussing the weather. And then she added simply, "You're my godfather and I love you." To her that seemed to explain everything.

Darby found words hard to come by and so he said nothing at all. He had never had to thank anyone for saving his life before and he just didn't know how to begin.

He still blamed himself for having been caught unawares. He had fallen into the trap of considering Little Italy as impregnable. It still was to strangers; but the Cortesis were not strangers. They lived there too. However, Darby's greatest failing was that he assumed everyone else would follow his own gangland code which was strangely chivalrous at times.

It had always been his proud boast that honest men had nothing to fear from him. When gang warfare broke out Darby chose the battlegrounds with care. It was important to him that innocent passers-by shouldn't be caught up in the crossfire. This was why he had been taken by surprise in Fratalanza. He just couldn't believe that guns would be fired in the crowded room of a club where men were wont to take their wives for a night out. The fact that the Cortesis had done so still amazed him. He could accept the wounding of Harryboy and the attempt on his own life as the start of a professional vendetta; something to be avenged, but not taken too personally. However, this careless attack in a family club filled with their own people was something else. In Darby's eyes, it put the Cortesis forever beyond the pale.

The Cortesis lived only a few doors away from the Fratalanza in Great Bath Street. But when a police constable attempted to arrest Harry Frenchie, he was obstructed by a mob who emerged from a French café on the other side of the road.

Gus Cortesi, the apparent leader of the mob, then attacked Doralli, who was standing alongside the constable, striking him several times in the face; and in the confusion Harry Frenchie escaped. Police reinforcements began to comb the dark alleys of Little Italy; and by the coming of the dawn, they had arrested the Cortesi brothers, Gus, Paul and George, together with Sandy Rice who was sporting a black eye … courtesy of Darby. Only Harry Frenchie remained at liberty.

Next day, the *Daily Express* reported:

"Scotland Yard detectives are still searching for the fifth man. He walks with a Charlie Chaplin step, the result of a combination of flat feet and knock-knees, but he is said to be able to disguise not only his walk, but his features.

Detectives believe that he took refuge in a house not a hundred yards from the Fratalanza Club, and emerged in the disguise of an old woman.

"He is a former bookmaker's clerk, about thirty-nine years old, sharp featured, about 5 feet 8 inches tall, with sallow complexion, brown hair, grey eyes, and a pronounced Roman nose. When he left the club he wore a dark suit, dark overcoat, and a light grey cap."

Later the same day, Harry Frenchie surrendered himself to the police station at Gray's Inn Road and was formally charged with the attempted murder of Harry and Charles (Darby) Sabini, by shooting.

Having been cautioned by Detective Inspector John Grosse, he had replied, "You know, Mr Grosse, I don't get mixed up in these things. It is not my game; but on Sunday night I was at my mother's house about midnight, which is a few doors from the club.

"I heard there was a row. When I went into the club everyone was struggling. Some were on the floor. I had not a gun. I heard a shot fired, and I walked out. I went to the Turkish baths. I often go there.

"The next morning I went to the city to see my employer, and about one o'clock my employer rang me up on the phone. He told me that you had been making inquiries for me, so I thought I had better come and see you."

As the man who had fired the shot which wounded Harryboy, he had of course been anxious to find out whether the Sabini was dead or alive before giving himself up. There was a world of difference between the charges of murder and attempted murder.

John Grosse, wise in the ways of gang warfare, had expected to find witnesses thin on the ground; and been pleasantly surprised to be proved wrong.

Purely as a formality he asked Darby whether he would be prepared to sign a statement. He had asked him that same question many times before, and always Darby had given him that golden smile and said nothing.

This time he simply said, "You write it out and I'll sign it." He never liked to admit that he could only read slowly and barely write at all.

Grosse asked curiously, "Is this because of Harryboy?"

Darby shook his head and it didn't seem as though he'd answer; but then he said, "With animals like these on the streets, there is no place for honest men."

But John Grosse wasn't the only policeman to be perplexed by Darby. Tom Divall, a Chief Inspector at Scotland Yard, had been waging his own campaign against the racecourse gangs, touring the country, confronting them when they were often mob-handed and he totally alone. A dangerous tactic in that day and age.

One afternoon at Hawthorn Hill, he challenged the Leeds Gang, who had introduced their own bookmakers to the course with skullduggery in mind. He pursued them relentlessly race by race, frustrating their plans. But then when the day was done and the crowds had gone, he became careless. With the light fading he walked out into the paddock and suddenly found himself surrounded by a hostile band of hoodlums who had been drinking heavily.

Sam Cross, leader of the faction, was holding a dagger in his hand. "You bearded us in our own den today," he told Divall, "and now you'll pay the price. Say your prayers, for you are about to die."

Divall backed away, looking desperately for an escape route, but there was none. The mob at his back pushed him roughly forward and Cross laughed. "How does it feel to be hunted for a change?" he asked. "To know you're going to die?"

Forcing himself to remain calm, Divall said, "You're drunk and you feel good. But how will you feel when you're sober and the hangman's waiting?"

Cross shook his head. "No one here will bear witness against me." And so saying he advanced upon Divall, dagger raised ready to strike.

And at that moment the ranks of the hoodlums were burst asunder and Darby stepped into the ring. "Be a sensible fellow, Sam," he said quietly, "and put it down. After all, who wants to wind up at the end of a rope?"

Cross's arm remained raised and he turned towards Darby with a curse. "Stay out of it, you Raddie bastard," he said, "or we'll bury you too."

Darby smiled, seemingly in no way offended. "Come on, Sam, it's just the ale talking. On another day you'll thank me for saving you from such foolishness. Here, take my hand."

He reached out his hand as though determined to make peace and, still smiling, hooked Sam Cross to the head. The blow was delivered with such force that the Leeds mobster was unconscious before he even hit the ground.

Darby's voice was still quiet and calm, but the smile had totally gone as he turned towards the mob. "Now pick him up," he said, "take him away and when he opens his eyes tell him that if he ever threatens me again, he'll be nursing more than a swollen face. I guarantee he'll never walk straight again."

There was the sound of running footsteps as other Sabinis, headed by Georgie Sewell and Massarda, hastened to join their leader. But it wasn't entirely this that persuaded the mob to pick up Sam Cross and hurry away. Darby was standing there with his hand resting on his hip, poised for action, and looking a very dangerous man indeed. The legend of the big gun which reputedly remained with him through the day and the night had worked its magic.

This legend also arose during the committal proceedings of the Cortesis' trial. From the very beginning everyone had sensed that the appearance of Darby as prosecution witness would be the star event. Defence advocates enjoy the cross-examination of known gangsters in the rival ranks; and Joseph Rankin was no exception. He was literally rubbing his hands together as Darby took the stand. He had done his homework on this self-styled king of Little Italy, and been struck by this legend of the big gun which Darby supposedly carried about his person at all times.

All he now had to do was put that thought in the mind of the jury; and the so-called murder bid in the Fratalanza would become nothing more than an affray between rival factions, both of whom were armed.

So Joseph Rankin asked his question, "Are you carrying a gun?" and a buzz of astonishment went round the court.

Darby opened his eyes wide, the picture of injured innocence. "Of course not," he said. "I'm a very quiet and peaceable man."

Rankin turned towards the bench full of confidence, sensing the coming triumph. "Your honour, I have reason to believe that the witness is lying. Do I have your permission to have him searched?"

Permission was granted and all eyes were on Darby as he raised his arms and patiently allowed two policemen to search him.

They found no weapon of any kind. The Cortesis' last hope had gone.

Darby left the court with a smile. Once again his marvellous antenna had served him well. As he went down the steps into the street, a henchman handed him back his gun.

As the trial moved on to the Old Bailey it brought the Mediterranean through the august portals of this, the most famous court in the land. The Cortesis, big, burly men leaned negligently on the dock rail during the proceedings. A succession of swarthy citizens with strange-sounding names paraded through the dock and a very English jury studied them in disbelief. But no one seemingly was more fascinated than the judge, Mr Justice Darling.

He prided himself upon being a linguist, fluent in both French and Italian; and at one stage in the trial, he addressed Darby in Italian. A look of pure astonishment crossed Darby's face. He hadn't understood a single word. After that the judge appeared to lose interest in the proceedings for a while. But during his summing up for the jury, he went to some lengths to explain that the Sabini family were the descendants of the Sabines — an ancient tribe from Central Italy whose women had been raped by the conquering Roman legions. He then added, apropos of nothing, that despite this unfortunate experience the women appeared to have fared quite well in the years that followed. He said that the present case reminded him of the old Italian feud between the Montagues and the Capulets.

Only two of the defendants, Harry Frenchie and Gus Cortesi, were found guilty; and they received the very lenient sentence of three years apiece for 'shooting with intent to murder'.

The jury had recommended that the Cortesi brothers should be deported upon completion of their sentences, but this was rejected by Mr Justice Darling, who said:

"I look upon this as part of a faction fight which has raged between you and the other Italians in consequence of some difference which the police do not entirely understand. You appear to be two lawless bands ... the Sabinis and the Cortesis.

"Sometimes you are employed against the Birmingham people and sometimes you are employed against each other. On this occasion you were carrying out a feud between you and the Sabinis. I have the power to recommend an order for your deportation. I am not going to do it.

"I can see no reason to suppose that you two men are worse than others who have been convicted in these feuds and have not been recommended for deportation.

"But the whole Italian colony should know of the Grand Jury's recommendation, and I wish to say to you all, if this kind of lawless conduct goes on, those who get convicted in future will be turned out of this country with their wives and children."

Darby celebrated that night in the Griffin, knowing that with the two Cortesi warlords behind bars, he was once more the undisputed king of his kingdom.

Louisa Doralli. She shielded Darby Sabini with her body and explained afterwards, "You're my Godfather and I love you"

THRILLING STORY OF THE SHOOTING OF SABINI.

Story Of Attack Led By Man In Shirt Sleeves
Brave Girl Commended.

herself between the th
man a ' an assailant an

Thrilling details of the shooting outrage in a club

GIRL'S HEROISM IN CLUB AFFRAY.

Stood In Line Of Fire To Save Sabini.

PISTOLS AND BOTTLES.

Thrilling Story Of A Midnight Attack In Clerkenwell.

Thrilling details of the shooting outrage in a Clerkenwell club, when
Harry S dangerously
wounded, were the local
court to-day,
appeared in

SABINI DRAMA HEROINE.

GIRL WHO SHIELDED HIM WITH HER BODY.

CONGRATULATED.

slightly-built, almost frail-looking,
dressed with neatness, described in
witness-box of Clerkenwell Police
yesterday afternoon how she threw
in front of a man as he was about
Charles ("Darby") Sabini in
Cleans Club, at the corner of
and Warren-street, Clerken-
night of November 19. She

"FRENCHIE" IN THE DOCK.

Four Brothers Cortesi In Shooting Charge.

"THE MAN MAY DIE."

Bail Refused: Detective's Story Of Arrests.

Mr Justice Darling rejected the jury's recommendation that the Cortesi brothers should be deported, stating: "You appear to be two lawless bands . . . the Sabinis and the Cortesis. Sometimes you are employed against the Birmingham people and sometimes you are employed against each other. On this occasion you were carrying out a feud between you and the Sabinis. I have the power to recommend an order for your deportation. I am not going to do it"

Derby Day, 1930. "By then, Epsom belonged to the Sabinis"

Sam Garvin (left) the Sheffield gang leader. "If Sam can make that sort of money belting people with a piece of lead," Darby proclaimed, "I can make twice that and never touch anybody"

The Griffin, headquarters of the Sabini gang.
"When their enemies came bursting into the Griffin, they would
be met by the boys in blue; and the Sabinis would sit on the bar,
smoking their cigars, watching the battle"

10

DEATH OF A FIGHTER

"Look clearly. This is the weapon my client faced on that fateful night" — Sir Edward Marshall Hall, brandishing a broken glass before the jury.

Barney Blitz, better known as Buck Emden, was standing at the centre of the bar in the Eden Social Club and there was space all around him. The denizens of this gangland haunt off the Hampstead Road had a nose for trouble, and Buck in such a mood could be very big trouble indeed. No one ever needed to explain that Buck had been a fighter, a bit too brave for his own good. It was written in the scar tissue of his face. He had been a contender with a big following in the East End, but those days were long gone. Now he was a lonely and a bitter man who spent much of his time brooding over past wrongs. A year earlier he had been charged with having caused an affray at Epsom and he believed that Edward Emmanuel, owner of the Eden and a Sabini associate, had informed against him.

Tonight he'd come to the club with the intention of confronting Emmanuel, only to find that the owner was out. So he waited and downed his lonely drinks, and with each passing hour his mood became more deadly.

Just before midnight Emmanuel arrived, accompanied by Alfie Solomons and big Harry Mansfield. Immediately, Buck turned from the bar and shouted: "Here comes the bleeding copper!"

Secure in the knowledge that he had a small army of Sabinis around him, Emmanuel threw the contents of a glass of beer into Buck's face. The fighter threw himself upon the other man, and both fell to the floor. Suddenly Buck pulled himself clear of Emmanuel, seized a glass, smashed it and drove it into his enemy's face. Emmanuel was helped to his feet, bleeding profusely. The club manager, fearful for his licence, urged them to finish the fight in the street outside, and the two men began to move towards the stairs.

But Alfie Solomons had also been drinking steadily that night; and as always, drink had transformed him from a reasonably sensible fellow into a vainglorious adventurer. He had risen with the Sabinis and took pride in his gangster reputation. That pride had been offended by the fact that this ex-fighter had dared to attack a man who had been in Solomons's company. He knew that once they were out on the cobbles, Buck would make short work of Emmanuel; and this would come as a further blow to his pride.

To Solomons in his drunken state the solution was crystal clear. Buck most not be allowed to reach the street. He withdrew a long, narrow knife from a sheath strapped under his left arm, moved silently across the floor and without any warning at all, plunged it into the back of Buck's head. Mortally wounded, Buck stumbled down the stairs and into the street. He staggered a few steps, then collapsed in the gutter. He was dead before he hit the ground.

Solomons was arrested and charged with murder before the hour had run its course. The death of Buck had sobered him, but only a little. He smiled confidently at the arresting officer, Sergeant John Clancy. "Don't worry," he said. "Darby will see me right."

Clancy, a big Irishman who had a certain respect for Buck Emden and none at all for Solomons, laughed shortly.

"Good," he said, "you'd better tell that to the hangman."

Sir Edward Marshall Hall was a portly, stagey figure; the last, the most expensive and the best of the prima donna advocates. He picked briefs which would best illuminate his singular talents as carefully as an actor selects his roles.

To the criminal fraternity he was 'The Guv'nor', a maker of miracles whose golden words could bewitch juries into giving verdicts which favoured the ungodly.

All of which explains why Darby Sabini made a concession when stepping into the advocate's flat in Welbeck Street, Marylebone. He took off his cap as a mark of respect and no one could remember ever seeing him do that before.

Sir Edward was wearing a monogrammed silk dressing gown and smoking a cigarette in a silver holder. His manner was brusque, but not rude. He was wise enough in the ways of the lawless to know that such men are unpredictable and not subject to the rules of society. If their feathers were ruffled they were quite capable of using violence against anyone, even King's counsel.

He said, "If you've come to talk to me on behalf of your friend Solomons, I must tell you that you're wasting your time. There is a proper procedure for such matters. You must approach the clerk of chambers and he will then offer the brief to whomsoever he considers the most suitable man for the job."

"I have already spoken to your clerk," said Darby. "He offered me Sir Roger Mortimer. I told him I wanted the best. I wanted you."

Sir Edward smiled slightly in acknowledgment of the compliment. He was studying Darby with some interest. He was too well aware of Darby's reputation to be misled by his peasant mode of dress. He knew that despite this apparent air of simplicity he was dealing with a very shrewd and a very dangerous man. He was genuinely interested to discover whether Darby would use threats or bribery in a bid to get him to change his mind.

"And what did my clerk say to that?" he asked.

Darby shrugged. "He said you wouldn't be interested, that it wasn't your kind of case."

"That man knows more about criminal law than anyone else in chambers. He understands the moods of judges, the quirks of juries, the qualities of even the most junior counsel. Yet you still doubt his judgment in this matter. Tell me why."

Darby answered this directly. "I distrust middlemen," he said. "In my experience, I have found that they are too anxious to protect their principals; and yet too lacking in wit and imagination to spot the opportunities from which great men can profit.

"I suspect that your man saw only the problems such a case can bring and none of the rewards. I suspect that once he realised a knife had been used by Solomons, he quickly made up his mind that the jury would bring in a verdict of wilful murder. He is a lawful man and therefore the notion of knives being used in a bar-room brawl would horrify him. I can understand that. They horrify me too."

He said all this without the trace of a smile and Sir Edward, who had heard of Darby's dislike of the traditional weapons of Little Italy, didn't smile either.

Instead he asked gently enough, "Why do you imagine my reaction might be a different one to that of my clerk? Don't you think that I might also find the thought of a knife driven into the back of a man's head with sufficient force to penetrate solid bone distasteful?"

Darby had of course realised all along that the two of them were playing a game, pretending that the clerk of chambers had made the original decision when it was common knowledge that this prima donna of an advocate would always have the final say. But it was the kind of game that Darby, that master manipulator of men, could play rather well.

"I came to you," he said, "because I know that you're a man of the world and that you therefore understand such things as this are not always the way they first appear. Rascals such as Solomons carry knives because they are forever in fear of their lives. Without such weapons concealed about their persons they feel naked, defenceless. If threatened they'll use them in the same way that a cornered rat will bite. I'm not defending the practice, but at least it's understandable. Now consider this man Emden. For him, there was no threat. He was a strong fellow, a good fighter who could have handled Emmanuel as easily as a grown man will handle a child.

"He had a grievance against him, so he could have beaten him with his fists. No one would have interfered. They wouldn't have considered it their affair. But instead he chose to smash a glass and then force the jagged ends into the face of Emmanuel. One would have thought that having scarred him for life he might have been content. But no, he wants to continue the fight in the street outside.

"Now if he was prepared to use a broken glass in the bright lights of a club, what might he have done down there in the darkness? Solomons believed that his friend's life was in danger and he acted foolishly, but then he's a foolish fellow." He paused. "And if all the fools on earth were to be hanged, it would be a lonely place."

Sir Edward puffed on his cigarette. "If you have such a poor opinion of this man Solomons, why did you take the trouble to come and see me?"

Darby sighed. "He has a wife, a good woman who doesn't wish to become a widow. He has two fine sons who have no wish to lose a father. They asked me to save him and I don't wish to disappoint them." He smiled wryly. "Of course I don't have that much power."

"But you think I have?" said Sir Edward, suddenly shedding his theatrical manner.

"I know you have," said Darby, showing his true force for the first time. "You have a greater power than police commissioners, a greater power than judges. Policemen can only send a man to court. Judges can only sentence him after the verdict has been reached. But you have the power to sway juries. They are, after all, simple fellows like me, merely putty in your hands. You can make them see the truth. So the power you have in a case such as this is one of life or death."

Sir Edward was finding the Italian's manner oddly entertaining and he was amused by Darby's description of himself as a simple fellow.

He asked cautiously, "And what would you suggest was the truth in this matter? What is the all-important message that should be implanted into the minds of the jury?"

"I am sure you already know," said Darby cleverly. "It's the choice of weapons. A knife may frighten the jury, but a broken glass will horrify them."

With that he reached into the inside pocket of his jacket, took out a thick wad of notes and tossed them on to the table.

"There's a thousand," he said carelessly, "just on account. I believe in paying top prices for top men."

Sir Edward made no attempt to pick up the money. "It's still my clerk's decision. Suppose he again advises me not to take the case?"

Darby was regarding him closely. "Talk to him as a man of the world," he said, "and I'm sure he'll change his mind. If not, keep the money. Regard it as payment for your time. I have no doubt you'll come to the right decision."

Both men already knew what that decision would be. Sir Edward's failure to hand back the money had virtually sealed the deal. Not even the most famous advocate in England would have dared take a thousand pounds of Darby Sabini's money and do nothing in return.

But in reality it was neither greed nor fear that had changed the mind of Sir Edward. He had already seen the dramatic possibilities of the case, already seen how he could achieve one of his greatest triumphs.

Thunder rumbled across the night sky and the rain began to fall as though intent upon scouring the streets of London. Anne Marlowe, sheltering under the canopy outside the Stardust, turned up the high collar of her mink coat and still shivered. There had been a time when the uniformed doormen would have rushed regardless out into the rain and whistled down the first passing cab for the lady, but not any more. Doormen merely reflect the moods of their bosses; and James Frazer no longer placed Anne Marlowe very high on his list of priorities.

The Rolls which had once been her daily chariot was now only used for very special occasions; and although he still kept a watching brief on the apartment, his own visits had become few and far apart.

She wondered whether it would be wise to return to the warmth of the club and wait for the rain to go away. She was still wondering when a red Bugatti swished into the pavement edge and the smiling face of Silvio Massarda emerged. "Hey, Princess," he called, "come and jump in. It's wet out there or hadn't you noticed?"

Without a moment's hesitation she ran through the rain and slipped in beside him.

"Did you whistle?" he asked. And she laughed remembering the words from another night: "Don't forget, Princess, any time you need me all you have to do is whistle."

She stretched out her long legs and sank back in the seat, lulled by his cheerful chatter. She watched his hands upon the wheel and knew instinctively that he loved this car as deeply as he'd ever love a woman.

"You haven't asked me where I live."

"The Penthouse, Park Lane," he replied simply.

"Are you sure you know the way?"

"Sure I'm sure. Everyone knows Park Lane."

"Then why," she asked reasonably enough, "are we going in the opposite direction?"

"Because I'm kidnapping you," said Massarda, laughing at his own joke. "Isn't that what rascals do?"

She knew that she should have been faintly alarmed. He was after all still a stranger and she hadn't forgotten the startling effect he'd had upon Alexander Levine.

Instead she decided to play along with him. "For ever?" she asked.

"One of these days," said Massarda, seemingly serious for the first time, "I think I will kidnap you for ever and never bring you back. But tonight I'm only going to steal you for a few hours. Buy you a good Italian supper, teach you to laugh a little. I've been watching you at the Stardust. You never smile any more, not with your heart.

"Anyway it's a crummy place, no good for you. I don't know why you go there." He paused. "And don't tell me you have no choice. Everyone has a choice."

She was looking at him curiously. "If it's such a crummy place, why are you always there?"

"Because you're there," he said. Then, as if anxious to lighten the mood, he added, "And another thing, Princess, I reckon I got to fatten you up. You're getting too skinny for a girl of mine. Mamma will see to that."

Mamma turned out to be the owner of an Italian restaurant in Kentish Town called aptly enough 'Mamma's'. No one ever called her by any other name.

She hugged Massarda to her ample breast and shrieked with laughter as he lifted her off the floor. He released her. "Hey, Mamma," he said, "meet Anne, the lady I've just kidnapped."

Mamma took a long look and then she nodded. "Silvio, you're getting some sense at last. You bring one very nice girl. But call her Anna. That a good Italian name."

She put her arm around Anne and walked her to the table. "You watch this Silvio," she said. "He very bad man." They could hear her deep chuckle all the way back to the kitchen.

Everyone in the place seemed to know Massarda. They called their greetings across from other tables, and when the waitresses walked by he pinched their bottoms in the most amiable way.

"Do you come here often?" asked Anne.

"Only when I've got a new girl," he said and added quickly, "Don't spoil the night by denying it. I've danced with you. I've kissed your hand. I've introduced you to my friends. I've fed you. Amongst my people, that's practically a betrothal."

"Don't believe a word he says," warned Mamma passing by. "He's a bad man."

Very much later he drove her home to Park Lane, displaying a fine regard for the speed limits of the city; and this time he was unusually quiet. Just for once in his life he was uncertain how to play out a scene with a girl.

He sensed that the dream and the reality were closer together now than they'd ever been before or might ever be again, and that one foolish action could so easily spoil it all. So far he'd only been play-acting. He was honest enough to see himself through her eyes. An amusing stranger who had chosen his moment well, arriving at a time when her world needed a touch of laughter. A mysterious buccaneer who intrigued her for the moment. But what would happen when the mystery was stripped away and she saw him for what he was … no buccaneer, just a gangster? Would she still be intrigued?

But because such thoughts depressed him, he shrugged them aside and by the time they stopped in Park Lane, he was once again his happy-go-lucky self.

She asked him up to her apartment for a drink and he surprised himself by saying, "Not tonight, Princess. If I came up you'd have to throw me out and you don't look strong enough for that."

He kissed her lightly and the kiss turned into something else. "See what I mean?" he said.

She smiled fondly. "Tomorrow I'm going to buy myself a whistle."

She was halfway across the pavement when he called, "Hey, Princess, remember next time I kidnap you it will be for ever. I'll never bring you back again."

Number One Court at the Old Bailey was filled to overflowing with the ungodly. For the time being old enmities had been shelved and they were banded together in the common hope of seeing one of their number escape from the clutches of law and order.

In the dock Alfie Solomons, all confidence drained away, looked as pale as death itself. And the jury looked almost equally ill at ease. For three long days they had been shown a violent world they had never known before. They had been shown pictures of Buck Emden lying on the pavement edge, his head surrounded by a pool of blood. They had handled the murder weapon, running thumbs gingerly along the razor-like blade. And all the while they had been conscious of those hard faces in the courtroom.

Only Sir Edward Marshall Hall appeared to be totally unconcerned as he began his closing speech. He had gambled by not calling the prisoner into the witness box, all too well aware of the fact that this could prejudice his entire case.

He reasoned that Solomons with his gangster mannerisms would destroy his own plea of self-defence and that under cross-examination he might well collapse. So Sir Edward pinned his hopes upon his own golden words and a bit of outrageous theatre.

On the table before him, he had placed an ordinary drinking glass. As he reviewed the events leading up to the fatal affray, he took leisurely sips from it. And then like the masterly actor that he was, he timed his moment to perfection.

He had just described the incident when Emden had smashed the broken glass into the face of Emmanuel. He paused and slowly drained his own glass, conscious that all eyes were upon him. He turned it upside down and then suddenly crashed it on to the table top.

Moving with surprising speed for such a portly man, he advanced upon the jury, brandishing the jagged crown of spikes before their eyes. Instinctively they recoiled as they saw the same cruel weapon that Emmanuel and Alfie Solomons had seen through the haze of smoke in the Eden Social Club.

It was a superb performance. The jury, putty indeed in the hands of this man, decided that Solomons had acted in self-defence and brought in a verdict of manslaughter. Solomons heard the sentence of three years' penal servitude and smiled in stunned disbelief.

Applause broke out around the courtroom and for once the ushers were unable to silence it. The wife, realising that she wasn't about to become a widow after all, wept tears of joy. Her two fine sons wiped away her tears. And then when her eyes were dry, she clasped her hands as though in prayer and looked not towards her husband, not towards Sir Edward, but towards Darby Sabini seated in the public gallery.

He gave her a brief flash of his golden smile, then lowered his head as befitting a modest man.

11

THE SWEET SISTERS

*"You'll see me in your dreams, Mikey. No matter
how long it takes, I'll be waiting for you" —
Georgie Sewell's grim promise to
Mikey Williams.*

The cavalcade of black sedans moved through the dark
streets of Little Italy. As the lead car turned into Saffron
Hill, its horn sounded a fanfare. The oil lamps were lit in the
houses and men aroused from sleep came spilling out into
the street, slipping their braces over their shoulders as they
ran.

The Sabinis were home from a raid on the Elephant
Gang and it was the kind of welcome reserved for conquering heroes. The soldiers stepped out of their cars and were
immediately surrounded by back-slapping admirers; and
inevitably the biggest crowd surrounded Darby. He stopped
there like a latter-day Roman emperor, smiling, handing
out largesse in the form of fivers which only a brief hour
earlier had belonged to his enemies south of the river.

Georgie Sewell stood watching the scene from the
pavement edge. He made no attempt to join in. He was still
the loner in the mob, owing allegiance only to Darby whom
he served as lieutenant, bodyguard and friend. It was an
arrangement that suited Darby ideally. He needed to have
someone close to him whom he could trust totally; and as
the Cobblestone Fighter had no wish to mix socially with
the Italian members of the mob, there could be no question
of a conspiracy.

Tonight Darby was a satisfied man and a proud one too.

He had taken care of his world, his people. His men walked the streets with their heads held high, their pockets stuffed with notes and silver, no longer the prey of any marauding bully-boy. Their women no longer had black dreams of rape. On their own streets, they were inviolate. And they owed all this to their golden-toothed protector who had now achieved the height of his powers.

He had three hundred armed men under his command. He controlled the racecourses of Southern England. Over half the London night clubs ran under his protection. The police had been corrupted as they'd never been corrupted before. And at long last his enemies had learnt to fear him, and for this he owed much to his cold-eyed lieutenant.

Georgie Sewell's philosophy was stark and simple. In the jungle of the underworld only strength was respected; and to this strange, lonely man respect was everything. So every threat made against the Sabinis had to be answered with actions rather than words.

In a series of lightning raids, the Sabinis proceeded to hit rival gangs where it hurt the most. The Irish Mob in Camden Town had seen their most lucrative night club, the Black Angel, torched to the ground. The Townsend Brothers, the vice lords of Paddington, had two of their brothels visited by the Sabinis, the girls and their clients driven into the street, too terrified to return. And tonight the Sabinis had smashed up six spielers belonging to the Elephant Gang and helped themselves to the loot.

Even the inevitable reprisals brought nothing more than a touch of light comedy to Little Italy. Darby, forewarned, would tip off the police. So when enemies came bursting into the Griffin, they would be met by the boys in blue; and the Sabinis would sit on the bar, smiling, smoking their cigars, watching the battle.

It had been important to Darby that tonight's raid should be completed by midnight. For this was the eve of St Peter's Day, and during the next twenty-four hours Little Italy would be a peaceful place. Darby would see to that. It was to be the day of the big Catholic Parade. The streets were already decorated with bunting and coloured lights. The women had laid out their best dresses in readiness and there would be presents for the children. On such a day you picked a pocket at your peril.

The Linden sisters had such beautiful, innocent faces that it made the heart of a man turn over just to look at them. As they strolled up the Clerkenwell Road chatting happily to one another the world seemed a better place for their passing.

Even the most lecherous of men felt a sense of guilt on noting the tell-tale jiggling of their bosoms, the bewitching roll of shapely hip, the rich promise of rounded thigh. The sisters had been gifted with that most devastating of all combinations, angel faces and bodies designed to torment mankind.

They had come to Little Italy to watch the parade, and strangers seeing them for the first time felt a fierce urge to protect them against all harm. Those who knew them rather better crossed themselves hastily and looked uneasily around. It was a safe bet that wherever the Linden sisters happened to be, the Williams brothers, Mikey and Johnny, would never be far away.

The sisters and the brothers were almost inseparable; and this was a constant source of amazement to the ranks of the ungodly. For even in the often brutal world of the London gangs, the Williams duo were considered to be beyond the pale. They had stabbed their own father to death with a broken bottle. They had cut off the toe of a child. They had scarred several women for life. And there were other rumoured deeds so dark that men talked about them only in hushed voices.

The cut-throat razor was the tool of their trade and they used it with sensual pleasure. When the mood was upon them, they would cut complete strangers for no apparent reason at all. They were simply men who enjoyed hurting people. With their awesome reputation they could walk into any pub and the bar would clear as if by magic.

At their chosen trade they were magicians. It was as

though the razors jumped into their hands and then disappeared completely once the cutting had been done. Several times they had been searched by the police in the aftermath of violence, but the razors were always missing. Men who had watched them at work swore that their hands never once went near their pockets. It was a mystery that confounded the underworld.

Today as always Mikey and Johnny were merely a few steps behind the Linden sisters, but they hadn't come to watch the parade. They were shadowing their next intended victim, Georgie Sewell. There had been bad blood between them for years. Even the nickname of the Cobblestone Fighter offended Mikey and Johnny. And his open contempt for what he termed the 'tool merchants' compounded that offence.

They had chosen this day with a certain cunning. Sewell, as one of Darby's hard men, would be keeping order on the streets, running his cold eyes over the villains. Then once the parade had finished and the crowds had gone he would be wanting his regular evening drink. Normally he would have chosen the Griffin where he would have been beyond harm; but Darby, the good Catholic, had closed the pubs of Little Italy for the day. So the Cobblestone Fighter would be doing his drinking beyond the confines of Clerkenwell. And if fortune was kind Mikey and Johnny would have the odds the way they liked them, two to one.

It was cool in St Peter's after the warmth of the day and Darby, a man who enjoyed the sun, shivered in the chill of evening. He picked up the offertory box, rattled it, listening to the lonely jingle of a few solitary coins.

There were footsteps in the aisle behind him. He didn't turn his head. He didn't need to. "I fear, Father," he said, "you won't be repairing many roofs with this."

James Delaney shrugged. "It may be many years before we reach our target. So patience has to be a great virtue; for we are surrounded by poor and hungry people."

"As you know," replied Darby, "I am also a poor man. But I am fortunate enough to have generous friends. Let me know your needs and I'll talk to them. I am sure we can come to an understanding."

The parish priest was intrigued by Darby's description of himself as a poor man. He was reputed to be earning twenty-five thousand pounds per annum from the race-courses alone. Delaney was also wondering uneasily whether such contributions would be made at the point of a gun.

So he asked, "Just where would these gifts for the church be coming from?"

Darby said reasonably, "Surely that's no concern of yours. A fiver will pass through many hands in its lifetime, be owned by hero and vagabonds, saints and sinners. But that's history. Surely the one thing which should concern us is the use that this money is put to tomorrow.

"It could be used to buy wild women, to pour more ale down the throats of foolish men, making them even more foolish than before. Or it could be used to give us all a church of which we could be proud."

He paused and asked cleverly, "What would you prefer?"

But of course there could only be one answer. And that was how St Peter's Italian Church in Clerkenwell came to be rebuilt with the spoils of a gangster army.

Georgie Sewell didn't even need to look around when Mikey and Johnny Williams came into the bar. One moment there had been people all around him; the next he was alone. He studied them in the mirror and was surprised as always to see the Linden sisters. They walked with the brothers to the far corner of the bar and gave no sign at all of recognition.

But he knew instantly that they had come to put their mark upon him. That knowledge didn't frighten him, because he had oceanic confidence in his own fast hands. Most of the villains he'd known carried their razors in their waistcoat pockets and it took a full second to draw them out. That had always been time enough for the Cobble-stone Fighter. He'd hook them to the head before anyone ever saw the blade.

Two men such as these shortened the odds, but there was still no real doubt in his mind. Mostly he was intrigued to see how they would go about their task. Their normal method was one of treachery. They would lure their victim into a false sense of security and strike without warning, often when a man's head was turned away from them. But he knew them too well to make that mistake.

He ran his eyes over the Linden sisters holding their handbags, looking so young, so vulnerable. It pained him to see these innocents in such company.

Eventually Mikey and Johnny joined him as he knew they would and the room had gone very quiet.

"I see you've joined the Raddies," said Mikey.

Sewell didn't even bother to answer. Instead he turned to the sisters. "Tell me," he said, "how two nice girls like you got tangled up with a couple of rats like these?" He used the tone of a man genuinely interested.

None of the onlookers gave so much as half a smile. They didn't dare. But they watched the faces of the brothers and saw the flash of madness in the eyes of Toddy.

The sisters smiled shyly and said not a word.

Sewell continued as though blissfully unaware of the effect he was having. "See what happened when you walked in with Mikey and Johnny? All the decent people moved out of the way.

"They want to do their drinking with men; not with a couple of cowards who need to come mob-handed before they can find the courage to pick a fight."

All this while he had been watching the hands of the brothers. But when the move came it was so sudden, so unexpected that he was momentarily taken off guard.

Johnny, with an unlit cigarette in his mouth, asked the girls for a light. And both unzipped their handbags as though glad the conversation had been changed. They fumbled for a match and out came the razors straight into the hands of their menfolk. It was so fast that only the Cobblestone Fighter saw it happen.

He hooked Johnny to the head by instinct alone, but the punch was so powerful that it knocked him straight over the bar. He ducked Mikey's slashing razor and felt it slice his ear as it whistled by. But in so doing he lost his balance and before he could recover Mikey clawed his nose with a broken glass, ripping through cartilage and bone.

With his face a mask of blood, he went after Mikey. But before he could reach him, three policemen burst into the bar and seized Mikey ... quite possibly saving his life.

Cheated of his prey, Sewell shouted, "I'll be there when they let you out in the morning, Mikey."

One of the policemen chuckled grimly. "You're going to have a long wait, Georgie," he said. "We're not concerned with this caper. He's got three separate counts of grievous bodily harm stacked against him."

And it was then that the Cobblestone Fighter spoke the words that would be remembered down the years.

"You'll see me in your dreams, Mikey," he said. "No matter how long it takes, I'll be waiting for you."

During the commotion, both the razors and the Linden sisters had disappeared.

12

THE DANCER

*"Machiavelli had a saying, 'Divide et impera' ...
Divide and rule ... That's what I suggest we do"*
— *Advice from Darby Sabini's college-educated
counsellor Alf White.*

Juan Antonio Castanar the Spaniard was seemingly a man
who had it all. He was lithe and handsome. He was rich. He
had a Rolls-Royce that caught the eye. He was reputedly the
best tango dancer in the world. And he had an army of
women who adored him.

Today at his dancing school in Archer Street, Soho, he
was putting the finishing touches to the routine of some
young dancers who were due to open at the Rio Grande in
three days time. They had no great talent, no inborn sense
of rhythm; but under his skilled tutelage they had developed a certain style. And in the smoke-filled Rio Grande
they'd get by. Most of the patrons of that rather dubious
establishment would after all be more interested in studying
legs than the refinements of a dancing technique.

The girls were in their late teens and early twenties, and
filled with dreams of distant stardom; sadly for most of
them, impossible dreams. But there was one girl named
Anna Monti who stood out like a diamond in a cluster of
glass.

She was the daughter of an Italian father and an English
mother, and it was from the mother that she had inherited
her blonde good looks and fair skin. She moved beautifully,
and there was an air of innocence about her, a desire to
please that would have touched the coldest heart.

When the rehearsal ended, Castanar beckoned to her. "You show promise," he said, and she positively glowed. "If you have the time, I would like to talk a little about your future."

For Castanar she would always have the time. She considered him more handsome than any idol of the silver screen, and so many of her dreams were wrapped around him. Like other stage-struck girls, she saw show-business as the great escape from a dreary world. In her case, an escape from the confines of Little Italy with its drabness and its poverty.

They had coffee in his flat above the studio and he embarked upon a well-practised routine.

"You know," he said, "one day you really could become a star in your own right; but nothing comes easy. You would need to be very dedicated, very single-minded; and I would quite understand if a young girl like you didn't wish to forsake the life you've led."

Anna almost stammered in her eagerness to reassure him. "No, no," she said, "dancing means everything to me. I want to be a dancer more desperately than anything else in the world. If need be, I'll work all day to improve." She paused, anxious to impress him with her modesty. "I know I have much still to learn."

"But how about the young men in your life?" he asked. "A girl as attractive as you must have many admirers. How will they feel about all this?"

Anna shook her head vigorously. "There are no men, no men at all," she said, and this was true. As part of her plan to shake off the shackles of Little Italy, she had steered clear of all entanglements ... gaining herself something of a blue-stocking reputation in the process.

He studied her thoughtfully, as she leant forward with her knees close together, so anxious to please. He let the silence drag out, then finally he said, tentatively as though still considering, "You know, I think it even possible that one day we could become partners and dance together on the stages of the world. The contrast in our appearance, the dark and the fair, might go well together."

He saw the dreamy look in her eyes and added hastily, "But first there must be much hard work. You will need the confidence that only experience can bring."

Later that afternoon he made love to her and she surrendered her virginity quite willingly, even with a certain eagerness, considering it a privilege to be bedded by such a demi-god as this.

In the weeks that followed, these afternoon sessions became a regular part of her life. Occasionally she would spend the entire night with him.

Her parents, who would have been outraged if she'd slept with one of the young bucks of Little Italy, accepted this liaison with equanimity, even in the case of the mother with some encouragement. Juan Antonio Castanar was after all a man of substance and the kind of son-in-law much desired by impoverished parents.

By the time the engagement at the Rio Grande had run its course, Anna was totally besotted. So when Castanar mentioned casually that he had booked the troupe on to a six-month tour of the Middle East, she was dismayed; for she had no desire to be separated from her lover. She told him so, and was unprepared for his sudden show of anger.

"At moments like this," he said, "I know I'm wasting my time and my talents. How can I hope to mould you into a star, if you're not prepared to make the odd sacrifice? Didn't I warn you that the road to the top would be hard?"

And then seemingly relenting a little, he added, "But I do understand that for a young girl such as you ambitions come and go. So don't worry too much. I am sure I can find a replacement for the tour ... and eventually, although it will be harder, I'll find someone else to partner me in days to come."

Faced with that unspoken ultimatum, Anna Monti felt she had little choice in the matter. She went on tour and Castanar saw the troupe off from Waterloo Station.

He kissed Anna goodbye, tasting the salt of her tears. "In six months, we'll be together again," he said, knowing that this was highly unlikely. For unbeknown to the girls in the troupe, they had already been sold into human bondage by a white slaver named Castanar.

It was a neat arrangement. In Cairo, his agents would take over. To preserve the pretence, there would be dancing engagements. They might even move along the road to Tangiers, supposedly their final destination. But somewhere along that road, the girls' money would run out, and one by one they would be fired. Then, penniless and a long way from home, they would be offered jobs as hostesses in shabby bars; and after that their decline would be swift and almost inevitable.

Castanar and his fellow vice czars had touched a rich vein of gold by discovering that in certain quarters of the globe the white woman was prized above all others ... and for the men smart enough to supply that rare commodity, there were fortunes to be won. The trade was worldwide, but especially viable in North Africa, India and South America.

Six months later, Alfredo Monti and his blonde wife Annie came knocking at Darby's door with their tale of woe. Alfredo, an industrious little man, had a baker's shop in Farringdon Road and showed a proper respect for this, the uncrowned king of Little Italy.

His wife was a little too bossy, a little too forthright, for Darby's liking; but he listened to them politely just the same. They explained that they had received just one letter from Anna at the start of the tour and it was now as though she had disappeared off the face of the earth. They had spoken to the parents of the other girls in the troupe, and they too had lost their daughters. So they had gone to Castanar and been received coldly. Out of the goodness of his heart, he'd said, he'd taught Anna to dance, taken a personal interest in her, found her work, created the chance of a new career. After that it was the responsibility of the parents to look after their daughters. Not his. He was, after all, a busy man.

Darby could see some reason in that argument, but one

point in their story still puzzled him. "Weren't you concerned," he asked, "when your daughter stayed overnight with this man, a man you'd never met?"

In such matters, Darby was very much an old-style Italian. He would never have allowed his own unmarried daughters to remain unchaperoned in another man's house, let alone spend the night there.

It was the mother who answered. "She wanted to marry him," she said, "and nowadays young girls go their own way. How could we have stopped her?"

Alfredo supplied a more honest answer. "Castanar had so much to give and we had so little. We just wanted her to have a good life and be happy."

This at least was something Darby understood. He nodded. "So just what is it you expect me to do?" he asked.

"Punish this man Castanar," said the mother, forthright as ever. "Make him sorry that he ever took advantage of such an innocent girl." Then she added cleverly, "Remind him that the girls of Little Italy are under your protection."

Alfredo bowed his head humbly. "Please use your influence to help us get Anna home again. That's all we want. Just to have our daughter home again."

Darby shrugged and spoke directly to the father. "I'll talk to this fellow Castanar and see what can be arranged. I'm sure that once things have been explained, he'll prove to be a reasonable man. So don't look so upset. Guard your health for your daughter's sake."

But there was self-interest behind Darby's gesture. International vice czars such as Castanar were already threatening to disturb the smooth-running of several establishments under the Sabinis' command. Two months earlier Castanar's main rival, Casimir Micheletti, a Frenchman known as 'The Assassin', had had the temerity to attempt to ply his trade within the bounds of Little Italy.

He had gone to the Italia, a night club under Nino's control, and approached the dancers and the showgirls, offering them the chance to tour Asia. He had made the tour sound wildly exotic, and mentioned sums of money which had hitherto been beyond their wildest dreams. Fortunately, Nino had been in the club that night and he had warned Micheletti never to cross the portals of the Italia again. Micheletti, who carried a stiletto, had looked at him calmly, shrugged and made no reply.

A fortnight later, Micheletti had been rash enough to send three of his most formidable henchmen to discuss terms again with the showgirls of the Italia. They had arrived in the early hours of the morning just as the club was about to close its doors. Nino and his followers — the same band who had once chased the Trimmer down the Clerkenwell Road — were waiting for them. The three men were beaten and striped, loaded into the back of a van and taken to Micheletti's house in Lisle Street, just to the north of Leicester Square. Nino had the trio, still only semiconscious, placed on the pavement with their backs propped against the wall of their boss's home. For the Sabinis, it was a standard gesture of contempt.

Castanar received Darby in his Archer Street flat coolly but without hostility, much in the manner of one businessman greeting another. He even offered him a glass of sherry which Darby declined, saying it was too early in the day for him. He didn't explain that sherry was one of the few drinks he'd never liked.

"So how can I help you?" asked the Spaniard.

Darby came straight to the point. "The parents of a young Italian girl called Anna Monti tell me she has disappeared somewhere on the road that leads from Cairo to Tangiers. You have to understand that Little Italy is a tightly knit community and many people come to me with their troubles. But this one is beyond my powers. So I have come to ask you this favour. Help these poor people find their daughter."

Castanar spread his hands wide, suddenly very much the Latin. "Of course I would if I could," he said. "But I have already spoken to the parents. I explained that this was simply a girl I taught to dance and for whom I found a job.

Once these girls go on tour, I lose touch. I tell you honestly, I wouldn't know where to look."

Darby smiled, but there was no warmth in the smile. "You mustn't insult my intelligence," he said. "I know that this dancing school is just a very clever front for your real activities; and I applaud you for it. Intelligent men are rare and therefore to be prized.

"You are in a business that I wouldn't wish to be in. But then how a man makes his living is no concern of mine." He paused, looked directly into the eyes of Castanar. "However, some of my people are not quite so understanding about such matters. Indeed, some tend to take the fate of this little Italian girl very personally. They have even uttered threats against you. Now as you know, I'm a peaceful man and I would be unhappy if trouble came between us. So I am asking you once again. Summon up all your powers and do me this one favour."

Castanar was meeting Darby for the first time, but he wasn't misled by the quiet voice and the talk of peace. He knew he was being given an ultimatum and one that he couldn't afford to ignore. The thing he didn't know was that Darby had already decided to remove these vice czars from his streets, quite regardless of Anna's fate. As he confided to Georgie Sewell, "They give crime a bad name."

So one night as the Eden was closing, he took aside his three most trusted men, Alf White, Georgie Sewell and Nino, and said, "Now tell me, how best do we get rid of these pimps and ponces?"

He looked first at the Cobblestone Fighter, who gently shook his head. Any advice he had for Darby would be given only when they were alone. He still preferred to be the loner within the ranks...

Nino was more forthcoming. "Place them in fear of their lives," he suggested, "and they'll run. These are not like ordinary villains. Frighteners are always the easiest ones to frighten." He said this soberly, quite forgetting that he was a frightener too.

But it was Darby's long-time counsellor, the college-educated Alf White, who would have the final word ... and this would prove to be oddly prophetic.

He said, "Machiavelli had a saying, 'Divide et impera' ... Divide and rule. That's what I suggest we do. Stir the pot and let these animals destroy one another."

Darby, who had never read a full-length book in his life, appeared to be immensely impressed. He always liked to hear White's quotations, and had made a point of learning several by heart. "Then that's what we'll do," he said.

Only Georgie Sewell knew that Darby had made that same decision days ago.

But first Darby waited patiently until Anna Monti had been returned to the bosom of her family, saddened but a little wiser in the ways of the world and no longer the dreamer of foolish dreams. He even sent Castanar a crate of champagne as a thank-you gesture to show his goodwill.

A few weeks later, Castanar's dance studio was burnt to the ground. And while the flames were still burning, Micheletti's headquarters at Le Mirage were also fire-bombed.

No one suspected the Sabinis. Instead, with false information being spread through the underworld grapevine, Castanar and Micheletti blamed the attacks on each other. Soon the two gangs, predominantly Spanish and French, were engaged in open warfare on the street. Stabbings and shootings became commonplace. Questions were asked in the House of Commons. The police rounded up the leaders of both gangs in a dawn raid, and both Castanar and Micheletti were deported; Castanar to his native Spain and Micheletti to Paris. But those warlike flames lit so skilfully by Darby continued to burn. Castanar travelled north in search of his enemy, found him one evening in Montmartre and shot him dead. He escaped the guillotine, but was banished to Devil's Island.

Jack Capstick gave the news to Darby, and the gold-toothed commander shook his head in wonder.

"God works his wonders in mysterious ways," he said.

"So does Charles 'Darby' Sabini," came the reply.

13

THE HEIR-APPARENT

"For that, I owe you something" —
Frederick Dew Sharpe, head of the Flying Squad,
speaking to Darby Sabini. "Maybe your life" —
Darby's reply.

By the thirties the Sabinis had gained a reputation for
ferocity which was out of all proportion to their actual
deeds. A stranger listening to the talk could well have
imagined that the rampaging hordes of Genghis Khan had
been let loose upon the city. In some quarters of the East
End, the cry "The Sabinis are coming!" could be guaran-
teed to empty a saloon bar in seconds or clear an entire
market-place.

This was a reputation which Darby did nothing to
encourage. It pained him that an organisation which had
initially been formed to protect his people should now be
looked upon as a terror machine. He recognised that it was
necessary to inspire a certain fear in the ranks of the
underworld, otherwise there could be no respect. But he
had no wish to put that fear into the hearts of ordinary law-
abiding citizens.

However, many of of the young bucks on the fringe of the
gang frankly enjoyed this new-found aura. It gave them a
sense of power they'd never known before. They traded
upon the name of Darby Sabini; and by so doing they
debased it. And none more so than Carlo Messina and Juan
Forcetti, two hulking young men whom Darby used occasionally and reluctantly as bouncers in some of the more
unruly dance-halls which came under his protection. He

had to admit they were good at their trade. Too good at times. More than once he'd explained to them that he preferred to have men talked peacefully out of the door, not beaten half to death, but they had chosen not to listen. They took pleasure in showing off their muscles, and without the violence the job would lose its savour.

Tonight Carlo and Juan were out on the town, strutting their stuff through Soho with an entourage of three youthful admirers trailing in their wake like a comet's tail. They were well aware of the figure they cut. Blazers tailored to emphasise wide shoulders, sports shirts open to the waist, gold chains around their necks.

They marched up Frith Street, very much an Italian stronghold, and went into Pardoni's, which was owned and run by a gentle old man called Alberto Pardoni. Despite his comparative wealth, he still dressed like the peasant he had once been. He would stroll happily between the tables, greeting his guests, jacketless and with a wide pair of braces holding up a pair of baggy corduroy trousers which had kept him company for twenty years or more.

The club reflected the tastes of its owner. The food was Italian. The music was Italian. And the customs were Italian too. There was a small band: piano, drums, accordion and mandolin. And tonight as always a young man named Angelo Gardini was the centre of attraction. He was both pianist and singer, and almost too handsome to appear totally masculine. His dark hair curled around his ears. His eyelashes were that shade too long, his face that bit too delicate. His body, lithe and slender, hadn't been built for strength. And his hands were clearly those of an artist.

His singing of Italian love songs touched the heart of Alberto Pardoni. It touched the hearts of the romantic younger women. It touched the hearts of the matrons who only wished they had been blessed with such a son. But it didn't touch the hearts of Carlo and Juan.

They had come to be admired, and they had no wish to share any of this with a gigolo of a piano-player. Upon their arrival they had taken the best table, one reserved for important guests. When Pardoni had pointed this out in that gentle way of his, they had simply waved him away. The old man had shaken his head sadly and shrugged, saying to his head waiter, "These young fellows today have no respect for their elders."

These unwanted guests continued to drink steadily, becoming increasingly noisy as the evening wore on. They play-acted for the benefit of their admirers, harrying the waiters, insulting their fellow-guests.

But they reserved their main abuse for the piano player, cat-calling, keeping up a hubbub of sound whenever he sang. Pardoni watched Angelo curiously from time to time to see how this might affect him, but if this too handsome young man was worried, it didn't show. His fingers slid effortlessly over the keys and his voice remained clear and unhurried. This apparent indifference angered the two Sabini toughs more than words could ever have done. The women still followed him with admiring eyes; and even worse, his style and panache was having the effect of making Carlo and Juan appear uncouth by comparison.

Eventually he finished his stint to a fine round of applause, took his bow and then strolled casually across the floor.

Carlo Messina sensed his opportunity. Now was the moment to strip away these romantic illusions and reveal this popinjay in his true colours. "Hey, pretty boy," he called out. "We're here to be entertained. You stop playing when we tell you and not before."

Angelo continued walking, getting nearer to them all the time. "No, I'm tired," he said, making himself sound humble. "I need to rest my voice a little."

It was then that the combination of too much drink and the gangster dream caused Carlo to do a very foolish thing. He took out a gun, saying, "If you don't want to sing, maybe you'd like to dance for us," and so saying he fired a shot into the floor only inches from Angelo's foot.

The piano-player moved faster than anyone present believed it possible for a man to move. In one panther-like bound he snatched the gun and using it as a club smashed it against the man's face. He did so with such force that the butt fell apart. Carlo slid unconscious to the floor, jaw broken, no longer a threat to anyone.

Juan reacted by instinct alone, reaching for the stiletto strapped under his left arm; but Angelo's reactions were the faster. With a whiplash action he brought the gun down on the upper arm with incredible force; and Juan's scream and the sound of breaking bone blended into one.

Before his companions could recover, Angelo had forced the gun hard and painfully against the teeth of Juan, who suddenly sat very still. But it wasn't the gun alone that caused this sudden stillness. It was the face of the piano-player. In the flicker of a second his entire personality had undergone a sea change. The almost too handsome singer of songs had gone, and in his place there stood a man so menacing, so deadly, that it took the breath away.

He let them all see the hunger in his eyes and then he said to Juan quite calmly, "You're a fifth-rate thug who stepped out of his league. Don't ever make that mistake again. If you or your well-muscled friend so much as put a foot across the doorway of Pardoni's, you're dead men. You had better believe me."

But this they had already come to understand. Being practitioners in violence themselves, they appreciated that there was a pecking order. This slim young fellow confronting them wasn't just another hoodlum. He was a killer. Wild horses wouldn't drag them across that threshold again.

Frederick Dew Sharpe, head of the Flying Squad, was by any standards a most unusual man. The underworld had dubbed him 'Nutty' Sharpe in recognition of the bowler hat he wore, tilted at a rakish angle. The newspapers had named him "the man who never forgot a face" — a reference to the seemingly photographic memory which time and again enabled him to pick out the villains in a crowd.

But his greatest claim to fame lay in the nature of his

arrests. They were the stuff of story books. When muggers were around he would stagger down dark alleys as human bait. He would battle hand to hand with some of the toughest hooligans in town. And he once had himself sealed into a crate which was then carried into a robbers' hide-away.

However, his most perilous moment came one day at Sandown Park when single-handed he confronted Darby and thirty of his followers.

There was no preamble. "I want you off this race-course," he said.

Darby smiled. "And what terrible crime," he asked, "have we committed today?"

"A bookmaker was beaten up by some of your thugs just half an hour ago," replied Nutty Sharpe. "That's all you need to know."

"Not quite all," said Darby reasonably. "Did this unfortunate fellow name his attackers?"

Sharpe tipped his bowler even more askance, a sure sign that he was growing angry. "He was unconscious. They have just taken him to hospital. That's why you and this load of rubbish are going too."

He was on very dubious ground and he knew it. It was a logical assumption that the bookmaker, a man with Birmingham connections, had been attacked by the Sabinis; but only an assumption, and it was a safe bet that he would never name his assailants.

Darby knew it too. He also realised that this was a showdown and therefore a difficult situation for both Sharpe and himself. Sharpe having made his move, rightly or wrongly, could not afford to back down. If he did, any authority he possessed over the racecourse gangs would have gone for ever.

On the other hand, Darby's followers were depending upon him to make a stand. In their eyes, he was omnipotent, with nothing seemingly beyond his powers. The situation was made even more difficult by the fact that Darby had achieved a certain understanding with the upper echelon of

Scotland Yard. Since taking over the courses of Southern England, he had come to be regarded as a moderating force. Gang battles at meetings were a thing of the past and violence was rare. As long as the situation stayed that way, the police (with the apparent exception of Frederick Dew Sharpe) were prepared to turn a blind eye towards his other activities. He had no wish to jeopardise that position. So he resorted to reason.

"I can understand why you're angry," he said. "In your position I would be angry too. This kind of nonsense gives us all a bad name. I don't believe any of my friends here have touched that unfortunate fellow. But if I am wrong and this bookmaker accuses one of them, then I pledge that I will bring the man to you to answer the charge. Will you accept my word on that?"

It seemed a reasonable compromise and Sharpe paused for a moment considering. Then one of the young bucks went and spoilt it all, asking arrogantly, "What do you say to that, copper?"

Sharpe, a man of few words, knocked him to the ground. Within seconds the mob had surrounded him, and perhaps for the first time he realised the true peril of his situation. Spectators were packing the distant rails watching the race. There were no witnesses in sight. Sharpe was totally alone. Yet he remained defiant, still standing his ground.

It was then that Darby remembered a distant day when he too had stood alone against the mob and been saved by the Cobblestone Fighter who admired gameness above all other qualities. Darby admired it too, and in his own strange way he also admired honesty. Sharpe possessed both these qualities to the full.

The mobsters had moved even closer, poised and hungry for violence. They were just waiting for the word and the lone policeman would be hammered to the ground and at their mercy.

But the word never came. Instead Darby said, "Come on, boys. We're off."

There were angry mutterings in the ranks, and for a

moment it looked as though they would defy their commander, but none wished to be the first to take that dangerous step.

Nutty Sharpe watched them file sullenly away and, still a little bewildered by this unexpected turn of events, he looked at Darby. "For that, I owe you something," he said.

Darby smiled. "Maybe your life," he said, and then he went too.

Darby was drawn to Pardoni's more out of a sense of curiosity than anything else. He wanted to make his own assessment of this piano-player who'd had such an alarming effect upon Carlo and Juan. Carlo's jaw was still wired together, his drinks being taken through a straw, and Juan's arm was in plaster. But although a week had gone by, the mere mention of Angelo Gardini's name still put fear into their eyes.

Darby arrived in the afternoon knowing that in clubland this was the quiet time of the day. Georgie Sewell was at his side; not because he sought retribution, but simply because the Cobblestone Fighter had become his almost constant companion.

Alberto Pardoni greeted Darby warmly, hugging him to his breast, and Darby — who was normally embarrassed by such Italian ways — put his hands on the old man's shoulders. Their friendship went back a long way. Pardoni had once owned an ice-cream parlour in Rosebery Avenue and Darby, just a slip of a boy, had swept the pavement outside every day. In return for this service, the old man would give him a Neapolitan ice cream.

It was just a token gesture. Pardoni, a kindly man, gave away his ices freely. It was merely that he believed they tasted even sweeter when a little effort had gone into the earning.

He now seated Darby and the Cobblestone Fighter at his favourite table, brought a pot of coffee bubbling hot from the stove and sat down beside them.

It was then that Darby did what for him was a rare thing.

He made his apologies. "The other night some men bearing my name disgraced themselves and me in your restaurant," he said. "I wanted you to know it will never happen again. I guarantee that."

Pardoni shrugged. "They make I think a big mistake; and that maybe is the only way some young men will ever learn."

At the far end of the restaurant, Angelo was playing the piano. As soon as he'd seen them sit down, he had made the melodies quieter so as not to disturb them. Darby approved of such politeness in the young.

Pardoni added, "Nowadays I am looked after by a very special young man."

Darby nodded equably towards the piano-player. "And that, I take it, is your very special young man?"

By way of answer, Pardoni called out, "Angelo, come and meet my friends."

Angelo ran his fingers down the keyboard with a final flourish and rose from the piano. Darby and Georgie studied him with interest as he came across the floor. Unlike Carlo and Juan, neither were fooled for a moment by his slender good looks. Instead they noted the leisurely stroll of a man supremely sure of himself.

Yet when introduced he showed a touch of humility, as befitting a young Mediterranean male in the presence of his elders.

Darby, more to test him than for any other reason, remarked, "So you're the young fellow who put two of my best men in the hospital?"

"I hope not," replied the boy.

"You mean you hope they're not still in the hospital?" enquired Darby, genuinely puzzled.

"No, I hope they're not your best men," said Angelo quietly. "Because if they are, I think you may be in big trouble."

He said this quite seriously, and yet for a moment there was just the hint of a smile in his eyes. Georgie Sewell chuckled, much amused. He had frequently labelled that strutting pair as "impostors" and this latest fracas only served to confirm that opinion.

"Perhaps they could profit from your wisdom," suggested Darby with gentle sarcasm.

Angelo's tone was still quiet, still polite. "Perhaps they could," he said. "After all, even dogs bark for a reason. So when a man waves a gun around in a crowded place for no reason at all, he can only be a fool."

The coffee pot had been emptied and Pardoni was just about to fetch some more when Angelo rose instead, placing a hand on the old man's shoulder. "I'll get it," he said. "You stay and talk to your friends."

Pardoni waited until he had disappeared into the kitchen and then turned to Darby. "I have a favour to ask of you," he said, and added with a smile, "maybe for all those ice creams I gave you long ago. I've already made arrangements to sell this restaurant and in a few weeks I return to Italy where I'll stay until I die. London is growing too cold for old bones. I need the sun.

"But I will be leaving Angelo behind and that saddens me; for he has become the son I never had. And I was hoping you could find a place in your organisation for just such a young man." He added hastily, "Not as a hired thug. He is worth more than that; but maybe in a club such as this where he could keep the peace."

"Doesn't he have any family of his own?" asked Darby, the eternal family man.

The old man sighed. "He comes from Palermo and his entire family died in a family feud. Five men, all brothers, burst into their house one night and killed them one by one. Only Angelo escaped."

"What happened to the five men?" asked Darby, suspecting that he already knew the answer.

"They've all gone to their graves," said Pardoni soberly. "That's why Angelo has to remain in London. The Italian police, like the Sicilian police, have warrants out for his arrest."

Even Darby and Georgie Sewell, who had lived their lives in a violent world, were a little awed by the story. But for Darby, a believer in destiny, the story had a greater significance. He had often thought about the day when he would have to hand over the reins of power to another. For a while he had intended to groom the loyal Nino as his successor. But Nino, despite all his good qualities, lacked the ruthlessness needed to run such an empire. Now by sheer chance this young piano-player had stepped into his path.

Darby believed that fate had been very kind to him.

Sandra Mancini had never known a day as good as this before. Most of her life had been spent within the confines of Little Italy. On the few occasions when she had gone out past its self-imposed frontiers, she had been accompanied by her mother or sundry relations. It wasn't considered either safe or proper for a young Italian girl to journey alone. Now, having spent the entire day on Epsom Downs, she felt like a caged bird who'd been given sudden freedom.

She was just eighteen, and like so many of the girls from the Mediterranean lands she had ripened early, in her case almost overnight. It was as though she had gone to bed as just another scrawny tomboy and woken as a desirable woman. She had only become fully conscious of that change when she saw the look on the faces of the boys as they watched her walking down the street. They had never looked that way before. Joyful at the transformation, she had turned into a natural flirt. Boys who hitherto wouldn't have granted her the time of day now pursued her ardently. It wasn't that she was a tease, although she gained that reputation. It was just that her mother, an old-style Italian, made sure that admirers kept their distance.

It was different on the Downs. She had arrived in a charabanc with the other Italian women, who had promptly settled down to a picnic in the sun and forgotten the very existence of Sandra Mancini. So she roamed freely past the swings and the roundabouts, past the bookies' stands, down the rails that fronted the grandstand to the point where the young Italian bucks were gathered under the command of Nino.

And everywhere she went she saw that look in the eyes of men. She became drunk on her admirers' desire. All her life until now she had considered herself a nobody. Now the knowledge that men wanted her tasted sweeter than wine.

She was wearing her very best dress, pink silk trimmed with lace. It had looked modest enough when her mother gave it to her for her seventeenth birthday, but now it was skin-tight.

Sandra would have liked this day to go on for ever, and she was still roaming happily when twilight fell. The Downs, highlighted by the twinkling lights of the fairground, had become a giant carnival.

She found the lorry park at the top of the Downs and was looking for the charabanc that had brought the Sabinis, when a rough-looking fellow stepped in front of her.

"Are you lost, darling?" he asked.

Before she could answer, there was a whisper in the darkness, "It's one of the Raddies' girls."

Instantly there was a rush of feet, and she was seized and lifted struggling into the air. For a moment she imagined this might be one of the tomboy games she'd played in the innocence of childhood. Then she was thrown bodily into the back of a truck. She screamed, but the wail of fear was swiftly silenced by a rough hand that clamped itself around her mouth.

She was aware of a sudden hive of activity around her. The engine of the truck roared into life. Men clambered hastily into the back of the lorry. The tailgate was raised, the flaps of canvas pulled across and they were rolling down the bumpy track beside the rails that led to the grandstand and the open road beyond.

She knew that she had to escape before they reached the end of that track; but she was held down as though by bands of iron. She tried to bite the hand that silenced her; but that hand had played this game before. It merely tightened its grip.

The scene was made to seem more eerie by the total lack

of sound in the back of the lorry. There was not so much as a whispered threat as it bumped its way past the evening crowds. The ride became smoother as they came to the road, and very soon afterwards an anonymous voice was saying, "All right, boys, we're clear now."

As if this was the signal they'd been waiting for, countless hands reached for her and within seconds the silk dress had been ripped away. Her first thought was one of sadness at the loss of that much-loved possession; but then as eager fingers fumbled with the clips on her corset, with the garter straps, panic set in. By the time they'd cleared the western outskirts of Epsom, she was totally naked. And that same anonymous voice was saying, "Steady, boys, take your time. It's a long road to Brum."

14

THE CLUTCHING HAND

*"What would you have said to the families of
these fine fellows you'd sent to the gallows?"* —
Darby Sabini, upbraiding his brother Harryboy.

Lady Diana Fenwick could have stepped straight out of the
pages of the *Tatler*. She was just about everything a socialite
could ever hope to be. She had been Deb of the Year two
long decades ago. She was well-bred, sophisticated, witty
and elegant. She was also very beautiful and very bored.

Two years earlier her husband had died when his
Bentley sailed over the rim at Brooklands. And it was only
after he'd gone that she realised how much she loved him,
how empty her life would be without him. In a bid to fill that
void she had gone on a leisurely world cruise. She had
busied herself with good causes. She had allowed some of
her admirers — the list was endless — to make love to her.
And she had still been lonely.

Now more recently she had found a partial answer. She
had opened a nightclub called the Charmaine in Charing
Cross Road on the frontiers of Soho and theatreland. The
need to work and to organise had helped keep her thoughts
away from the past, and with people around her she was no
longer quite so lonely.

So far everything had run smoothly, with just one minor
irritation. Her manager Jamie Andrews had informed her
that a band of Italians known as the Sabinis had offered to
protect the club from harm and wished to be paid for so
doing. She had stated flatly that she didn't need protection,

and had been surprised at the sudden alarm in Jamie's eyes. So more on a whim than anything else, she had said that she would meet the spokesman of the Sabinis and explain the situation herself. She foresaw no problems.

Now that she was sharing a table with Darby, she could still see no problems. She had been frankly disappointed in this, her first acquaintance with a so-called gangster. She had expected a more dangerous-looking man, someone more forceful, more commanding. In fact, Darby appeared at his worst. He was being a little too simple, a little too peasant-like in his greeting.

A band of fellow-Italians, clearly his followers, were seated a few tables away; and she was surprised to see that they were better dressed than their leader. A little flashy perhaps by her standards, but nonetheless there was something mildly romantic and adventurous about them.

Darby by contrast in his dark clothes and black muffler appeared almost drab. She couldn't be expected to know that this was his protective colouring. The world of the socialite was something that as yet he didn't understand, and so as always when unsure of his ground, he preferred to be taken for a simpleton. But his eyes had missed nothing. He had taken in the elegance of the club, its potential for money-making, its vulnerability for the likes of him. And he had taken in too the elegance of this woman, leggy, slender, tall, nimble and with that unmistakable air of one used to being obeyed.

She came directly to the point. "My manager tells me that you have offered us protection. I told him that we had no need of that protection, but I thought it only courteous to tell you myself."

"And did he agree with your opinons?" asked Darby. Lady Diana shrugged. "I don't know. It was my decision. I didn't ask for his views."

"Maybe you should have done," suggested Darby, his voice mild, almost apologetic. "This is a rough part of London which he knows well. He has been with other clubs before. During the daytime the streets are peaceful enough.

Men can go about their lawful business. But at night there are ruffians everywhere and a place like this attracts them.

"You have beautiful women and a lot of money coming across the bar, and they like those things. But because these ruffians have never learnt respect, they drink too much, they threaten, they fight and they steal; and very soon, I think, you don't have a club any more."

The aristocratic face was impassive, polite. "Just suppose for a moment that you are right and that we do have trouble. Then why shouldn't I call the police? The Commissioner was a personal friend of my late husband. You may have heard of him." There was just a trace of sarcasm in her voice.

Darby ignored the sarcasm. "Of course the police would come. But by the time they arrived the ruffians would be gone, so what could the police do? They would ask questions, but how would that help you? Very soon all these nice people who are your guests would decide to go to other clubs where these sort of things don't happen."

Lady Diana smiled slightly. "You mean they'd go to clubs who are already paying you to protect them?"

Darby acknowledged the truth of that with a shrug.

She was still smiling as she said, "Just supposing I tell you to go to hell, what would you do? Would you have my men beaten up? Would you have me slashed with a razor or maybe raped? Isn't that the pattern?"

Darby said gravely, "That's the worst kind of nonsense and you know it. I expected something better from a woman like you."

She had been playing a game, a little intrigued by the twilight world of the gangster, but now she was tiring of that game and growing angry.

"All right, another question. What do you imagine would happen to you if I told the Commissioner that you'd been bothering me?"

Darby spread his hands wide and suddenly looked very Italian. "I don't understand you. I came here at your invitation to discuss a business proposition. Have I made one single threat, offended you in any way?

"I have merely offered you a service which you may accept or reject as you wish. To tell you the truth, your decision is no great concern of mine. By all means talk to your friend the Commissioner. I have nothing to hide. I am simply a businessman."

"And can I tell him what line of business you may be in?"

"My business is controlling ruffians," replied Darby perfectly seriously.

There came a burst of laughter from the Italians enjoying some ribald joke at their nearby table. Darby turned, gave them the merest glance, and they sobered instantly.

The gesture didn't escape the attention of Lady Diana, who had begun to re-evaluate her opinion of this apparently simple man who could command such instant obedience.

Her anger was now mixed with curiosity. "I have twelve men working for me here. Twelve honest, loyal and able-bodied men. Suppose I told them you were bothering me and asked them to throw you and your friends out into the street. What would you do then?"

Darby smiled, genuinely amused, gold teeth glittering, and said nothing. But then he didn't really need to. That confident, careless smile had been far more effective than words. And for the first time Lady Diana glimpsed the true force of the man.

Then almost as an afterthought he said, "If you really want me to go, there could be a much easier way. All you have to do is ask us and we'll leave. After all, we're not villains."

Before she could reply, an argument broke out at the bar. A large and obviously drunken man had laid careless hands upon a woman in evening dress. And when her husband complained, the large man had struck him above the left eye, causing a three-inch gash and a sudden rush of blood.

The wife had screamed and a waiter attempting to seize hold of the drunk had been flattened with contemptuous ease. The drunk had added drama to the scene by smashing a glass and holding out the jagged end towards his fellow-guests, who were fanning out into an ever-increasing circle.

In the stunned silence Darby's quiet voice carried across the room. "Angelo," he said. And Angelo rose, left his fellow-Italians, walked casually across the floor towards the bar, avoided the drunken lunge with practised ease, seized the arm, allowed the glass to drop and then just as casually walked his man out of the door and into the night.

Darby, who had been watching all this with only mild interest, turned to Lady Diana. "You see what I mean," he said. "Nowadays there are ruffians everywhere."

But of course by now she had already begun to understand. "If you did protect me, how would you prevent scenes like that?" she asked.

Darby considered the question carefully. "I would give you my best man. I would give you Angelo. He would be here every night. You would be simply paying his wages." He paused. "Rather generously, of course. He is a smart and rather special young man."

In her mind's eye Lady Diana could still see Angelo walking so casually, so confidently across the floor. She considered the image romantic and daring. She agreed instantly.

The arrangement suited Darby rather well. Ever since that first meeting in Pardoni's restaurant, Darby had believed that this was the one destined eventually to take his place. He was afraid of nothing, but the quality which impressed Darby most of all was his intelligence. He had an almost instant understanding of everything required of him. As a first step, Darby had already begun to groom him for a position of command within the mob.

He hadn't as yet realised the real reason why Angelo appealed to him so much. Angelo in so many ways was a youthful edition of himself. The Charmaine would be an ideal setting for him to learn another facet of his trade. He would be mingling with socialites who would be a far cry from the people of Little Italy, and this was good too. Darby had already decided that this was a world in which there was money to be made; and therefore a world which he had to enter.

Darby sealed the agreement with a handshake and left the Charmaine a few minutes later, his men following quietly. They walked a hundred yards up the street and into the bar of the Albion where the large, drunken man was standing, a full glass in his hand. Only this time he seemed remarkably sober.

"How did I do?" he asked.

"We'll make an actor of you yet," said Darby smiling, and quietly as ever slipped two fivers into the man's top pocket.

You only had to look at the barbershop of Jimmy Sabatini on this bright July morning to know that all was right with the world. There were smiles on the faces of customers and barbers alike, while Sabatini whistled cheerfully through his teeth as he sharpened his favourite razor against the heavy leather strop. All of which was a little unusual, for he was not by nature a cheerful man. His right hand had been malformed since birth into the shape of an eagle's claw; and because of this he nursed a grudge against God and the entire human race.

He was known throughout the Italian community as 'The Clutching Hand', and all day long that hand would shake as though it had the palsy. Yet as soon as he picked up a razor, the tremors would go away and the hand become as firm as the proverbial rock.

Tomorrow he would hang a closed sign upon the door and take the north-west road; and this was the cause of his present cheer. He would be heading a team of Sabini toolmen sent by Darby to take bloody vengeance upon the Birmingham Boys.

The abduction and gang rape of Sandra Mancini had sent shock waves around Little Italy. Young bucks who would slit a throat with a song on their lips were outraged by this piece of sexual plundering.

Matrons who never missed a Mass wanted the culprits

delivered into their hands. A little delicate knife work would guarantee that they never bothered a poor benighted Italian girl again, or any girl for that matter.

Some of their menfolk wanted an eye for an eye, the abduction of one of the Birmingham mobsters' wives, preferably a young, pretty one.

Darby shook his head sadly at such talk. "What kind of men are we supposed to be," he asked, "who wish to make war on women? A man who doesn't respect the wives and the children of other men, no matter how vile those men may be, is no kind of man at all. Leave that kind of nonsense to the Birmingham Boys who are, after all, nothing more than a band of pimps."

The use of the word 'pimp' had always been Darby's most extreme form of abuse, because with his strait-laced morality he could conceive of nothing lower than a man who lived off the immoral earnings of a woman.

Some of the more hawklike Sabinis were demanding an outright war that would only end with the death of the abductors; and Darby's youngest brother Harryboy was the leader of this faction. He was a big, florid, handsome man who caught the eye. More than any other member of the Sabinis, he looked the part of the traditional gangster, strong as a bull, bold and quick to anger.

He favoured open-necked sports shirts in vivid hues, tailored suits that emphasised the wide shoulders and narrow hips; and he took particular pride in his highly polished spring-heeled boots. There was bravado in Harryboy, but there was courage too. True, he hadn't emerged with much credit from that one-sided bout with Georgie Sewell; but this was as much due to superstition as anything else. Like many of the Italians, he looked upon the Cobblestone Fighter as an irresistible force, something beyond the reach of mere mortals.

The younger Italians idolised him, but many of the older ones looked at him askance. They feared that those impulsive ways would one day bring ruin to them all.

It was typical of Harryboy that he should raise the matter

of vengeance with Darby in the crowded bar of the Griffin. Even though it was after closing time, there were men there who were at best only fringe members of the mob; and Darby normally only discussed tactics with his trusted inner circle. He had already established a chain of command in which he would give orders direct to Alf White, who would pass them on to one of the lieutenants, usually either Massarda or Ginicoli, and so on down the line.

That way it became impossible for the police ever to trace anything back to him. All he had to do was break one link in that chain and he was totally secure.

Now, although he was annoyed with his brother, he gave no outward sign of that anger. Harryboy had been drinking heavily, and although he wasn't drunk, whisky had loosened his tongue.

"The boys want to know when we're gonna hit Brum," he said. "All this is making us look bad. It takes us back to the days when any nobody could come hunting the half-assed Raddies and know he was safe. Now a band of strangers have tried to kill you on the Downs. They've grabbed the Mancini girl and taken turns banging her all the way home to Brum, just because she's an Italian.

"Everyone has been sitting back waiting to see what we'll do about it and so far we've done nothing. It's like giving them an invitation. After all, we've a lot more little Italian girls they can come and rape if they're getting a taste for that kind of thing. I say we ought to kill the ponces now, show 'em we mean business."

A murmur of approval ran around the bar and Darby smiled slightly, but only with his lips. "So how do we do that, brother of mine?" he asked.

Warmed by the backing of his admirers, Harryboy ws beginning to adopt the trappings of leadership. "No spankings this time," he said, "no dusters, no knives, no razors, just guns.

"The one thing they won't be expecting is a raid on Brum. I've checked their movements and the routine never changes. Every lunchtime they drink in the George on

Radley Street, then at closing time they go up upstairs and play billiards. They stay there all afternoon. That's the time to hit them. They have us figured for a bunch of rats. With a dozen guns we could finish the lot of them, then be back in London by the evening and we could have a hundred witnesses prepared to swear that we'd been here all day. Anyway, why should the law care what happens to a bunch of pimps like that?"

The bar had gone very quiet and everyone was looking at Darby.

"So if I'd been killed on the Downs," he said, "and you'd taken my place, this would have been your move. Is that what you're saying?"

Harryboy shrugged. "I'd have done it the next day. That way everyone would have seen what happens when you mess with a Sabini."

Darby's voice was as quiet and peaceful as ever. "Guns make a noise. There would have been a crowd on the pavement. What would you have done about that?"

"Did anyone try to stop us on the Nile?" asked Harryboy slyly. "Did anyone bear witness?"

"That was a spanking," replied Darby shortly, "not a murder. We were all careful not to shoot to kill."

The discussion had turned into a battle of wits between the two brothers, and by now just about everyone in the bar had come to realise the true issue at stake. It was the future leadership of the Sabinis. If Harryboy could overrule Darby on this vengeance raid, it would only be a matter of time before he ousted him entirely.

But the younger brother was being steadily outmanoeuvred. He played his last card. A woman had been disgraced, he said. "No one could call it murder. It would be an affray, self-defence."

Darby no longer bothered to hide his contempt. "You walk into another man's backyard with a gun in your hand and then expect a jury to call it self-defence? Sometimes I think all that drinking must have turned your brain soft. You've been talking like a Sicilian. Maybe in Palermo you could kill a man for dishonouring a woman, and policemen would look the other way. But like me you've lived your life in England, and if you'd opened your eyes you'd have known it isn't like that over here. If you kill a man in England, it makes no difference how evil that man may be. They still call it murder. They put a hood over your head and a rope around your neck, then they open the trap."

He paused and looked directly into his brother's eyes. "So tell me," he said, "after you'd played this comedy of yours, what would you have said to the families of these fine fellows you'd sent to the gallows? What comfort would you have given the widows? How would you have dried the eyes of the children?"

All around the room men were shrugging and shaking their heads over the foolishness of Harryboy, who had finally come to realise that he'd walked into a trap of his own making.

He took a step closer to Darby. "All right, if you haven't the stomach for guns," he said bitterly, "what are you going to do?"

"When I judge the time to be right," said Darby, "I'll do what has to be done. In the meantime I have no wish to discuss my plans with a fool."

It was only then that Harryboy understood the enormity of his mistake. In his own quiet way Darby had become a despot. He would allow no man in Little Italy to question his authority. He was outraged by the fact that the first one to have done so was his own brother.

If Harryboy had ever had any chance of becoming his right-hand man, that chance had now gone for ever. The younger brother would have no part in the counsels of the older. It was a mark of this changed status that Darby failed to tell him that orders for the vengeance raid had been given the previous day.

The last reluctant drunk had just been ushered out into the street; and Mike McKay, landlord of the George on Radley Street, sighed with relief. He never enjoyed the lunchtime

Sir Edward Marshall Hall. "The most expensive and the best of the prima donna advocates. He picked briefs which would best illuminate his singular talents as carefully as an actor selects his roles"

Oct. 2, 1924

THE DAILY MIRROR

GRAPHIC STORY OF CLUB STABBING.

Accused Said To Have "Darted Like Lightning" with Knife.

"DEAD MAN'S FEARS."

Graphic stories of the fatal club stabbing were related when the inquest on Barnett Blitz (also known as Buck Emden), the bookmaker, who was di........... lying i...

CLUB TRAGEDY

Harry Mansfield, a witness yesterday.

HOLBORN GUARDIAN

VERDICT IN CLUB STABBING AFFRAY

SENTENCE OF THREE YEARS' PENAL SERVITUDE FOR MANSLAUGHTER

Alfred Solomons (31), hawker, of Gerrard street, W.1, was found guilty at the Old Bailey on Tuesday, of the manslaughter of Barnett Blitz, a bookmaker's runner, of the Eden Social Club, Eden-road, Hampstead-road, N.W.1, last September. He was sentenced to three years' penal servitude.

Solomons was indicted for murder, but the judge..... to the jury the circumstances which..... found.......

STABBED BOOKMAKER.

At the resumed inquest yesterday on Barney Blitz, a bookmaker, who was found fatally stabbed in Eden-street, Hampstead-road, N.W., Harry Mansfield, a witness, was asked by Mr. Sharman, representing the dead man's relatives, if he had any cause to fear for his own safety after Blitz's death.

Mansfield: What have I to fear? I have never had a row with anyone in my life.

Mr. Sharman: Did this lead to your committing a foolish act?!

Mansfield did not reply.

The inquest was adjourned.

Alfred Solomons 31, a fruit salesman, of Gerrard-street, who has been remanded on a charge of murdering Blitz, was present.

Alfred Solomons accused of the murder of Barnett Blitz, the bookmaker stabbed at the Eden Club, Hampstead - road. Graphic stories were told at the inquest yesterday.

Alfie Solomons (bottom right). "When charged with murder, Solomons smiled confidently at the arresting officer. 'Don't worry,' he said, 'Darby will see me right'"

Pasquala Poppa (left) alias Bert Marsh. "He had been good enough to put Pete Herman on the floor during sparring before Herman's fight with Jimmy Wilde for the flyweight championship of the world"

The Catholic Parade with St Peter's Italian Church in the background . . . "a church reputedly rebuilt on the proceeds of a gangster army"

trade. There was too much hustle and bustle and looking at watches.

He could already hear the clink of ball upon ball in the first-floor pool room which served as headquarters for Harry Bates and his enforcement wing of the Birmingham Boys. He would have liked to have gone up there and played a game or two himself, but he decided that this wouldn't be a wise thing to do. The Boys had been showing a mean streak ever since their last raid on Epsom. They didn't encourage outsiders like Mike any more.

He was surprised to hear a knock upon the door. But when he opened it he found a small band of men with cue cases in their hands.

The leader of the band, a small man with a leathery face, smiled briefly. "Harry's expecting us," he said and walked straight through the bar as though that was explanation enough. They had the hard look that Mike had come to know, the look that doesn't encourage questions.

As they filed past him, he said pleasantly enough, "Harry's in form. He'll take some beating."

"Don't worry," said the small man, "we'll find a way." And at this muffled laughter ran down the line.

Mike went back behind the bar and wondered idly how the small man could play billiards with that clawlike hand of his. He had never seen a hand shake so badly.

Meanwhile up on the landing the Sabinis had opened the cue cases and taken out the shotguns.

Jimmy Sabatini, the Clutching Hand, was the first to step into the pool room. "Hello, Harry," he said, "we've come to give you a game." As always he was immensely cheerful when the work was about to begin.

Harry Bates half-raised the cue as though to crash it against the head of Sabatini, but froze as he saw the shotguns coming through the door.

The Birmingham Boys were swiftly lined up against the wall and Bates stared at the guns with a fearful fascination.

"Those things go off like cannons," he said. "Use them and you'll have the place surrounded."

Jimmy Sabatini spoke in seemingly friendly fashion. "Don't worry, Harry, they're just our insurance." The honed razor was already in his hand, and that hand was as steady as a rock.

15

THE GODDAUGHTER

"It was the men who failed to kill me on the racecourse who took a coward's revenge upon your daughter" — *Darby Sabini addressing the parents of Sandra Mancini.*

Sandra Mancini's return to Little Italy had produced mixed emotions in the community. To many of the young bucks she was now a scarlet woman. They'd see her walk on by, and unbidden would come the images of that long night ride to Birmingham. And they'd wonder whether she'd screamed or sighed and cried out for more. A gang rape was so far beyond the experience of them all that they invested the tawdry event with a certain glamour.

The young girls, some of them the most virtuous of maidens, were curious too. The notion of being overpowered by a band of rampaging men filled them with fearful fascination. They would slyly ask their questions and Sandra would answer with a scornful toss of the head.

The young matrons with their own teenage memories not far behind were sympathetic; it was the older women who were the cruellest. To hear them tell it, Sandra had brought shame upon her race.

They remembered the too-tight dress she'd worn at Epsom and chose to forget that it was the only one she had. And as for Sandra's parents, cursed with that most pernicious of social sicknesses known as respectability, they cast her out of their house.

She promptly proved her wisdom by calling upon Darby for his help. He listened to her tale of woe and then he said,

"I can give you some money to help you move, is that what you want?"

She shook her head. "Where would I move to in this city?" she asked. "Little Italy is the only place I know." And then she added slyly, "Look what happened to me last time I fell into the hands of strangers. No, I have only one wish. I want you to talk to my parents and persuade them to let me stay."

Darby was amused by her directness. He considered it an admirable virtue in one so young. "Consider it done," he said. "Tonight you can stay in my house with my family. Tomorrow I will visit your parents and sort out this little misunderstanding. They are good people and I'm sure they'll listen to me."

He found it astonishing that any parent could ever deny a child a roof over her head. If his own children had committed murder he would still have shielded them.

So the following day he called upon the parents of Sandra Mancini and was welcomed with a flurry of activity. After much shaking of hands, the father hurried off to fetch the wine and the cakes, while the mother hastily slipped on a freshly laundered tablecloth. Darby had become a very important man in the community.

After politely toasting the health of his hosts he came straight to the point. "Last night I gave your daughter shelter in my house, because she tells me you no longer wish to shelter her in your own.

"I know that you are reasonable people. So I ask you to grant me this favour and allow me to act as mediator in this matter. I am sure you have no true wish to lose a daughter."

It was Mamma Mancini who answered, and immediately Darby knew who made the decisions in this house.

"I thank you for your interest, but you don't know our daughter as we know her. You see her from time to time on the street and no doubt she'll smile politely as she goes by. But there is a demon in her that only I as a mother can see. Ever since she was a young girl she has fed on the admiration of men. I have seen that look in her eye when a handsome-looking man steps on to the street. I have guarded her and tried to keep her from harm, but there is a wickedness in her that will out."

Darby nodded politely. "As the mother of a grown-up girl you understand such things. My own daughters are still too young for such foolishness.

"But isn't it possible that you are judging her a little harshly? The world is changing, and isn't it only natural that such a fine-looking girl should enjoy a bit of admiration?

"You must understand that I feel a certain responsibility in this matter. It was the men who failed to kill me on the racecourse who took a coward's revenge upon your daughter." He paused. "I must confess to a certain fondness towards her. If you would take her back out of the goodness of your hearts, I would be honoured to become her godfather."

It was cleverly done. There wasn't a family in Little Italy who wouldn't have been delighted to have Darby as the godfather of their children. After all, just think how this had changed the life of Louisa Doralli. Naturally, the Mancinis agreed instantly.

No Sir Galahad ever defended women with more chivalry than Darby Sabini. So when he learnt that a gang of pickpockets from Bethnal Green was specialising in the lifting of women's purses, he shook his head sadly.

"I just don't know what the world is coming to," he told Silvio Massarda. "Such men give villains a bad name."

"Shall we go and give them a spanking?" suggested Massarda, who was becoming a little bored with life at the top of the gangster tree. "Teach them the error of their ways?"

Darby considered the idea for a long moment and then shook his head. "No, I know a better way. I'll talk to Nutty."

Few statements could have surprised Massarda more. For of all the detectives trailing the Sabinis, no one was more determined to bring them down than Nutty Sharpe.

But Darby had been wise enough to realise that the two

of them had at least one thing in common. Sharpe was chivalrous too. He also owed his well-being, if not his life, to Darby.

A few days later, Nutty Sharpe followed this gang of nine pickpockets on to a crowded bus and ordered the driver to "drive straight to Bethnal Green police station and make no stops along the way."

Very much to the astonishment of passengers and pickpockets alike, the driver proceeded to do just that. As the bus drew up outside the station, a dozen policemen filed out parading for duty. Commandeered by Sharpe, they surrounded the bus and the pickpockets were taken into custody one by one. A debt had been repaid.

Wallflowers come in all shapes and sizes. Sometimes they are tall girls who make even the strapping fellows seem small by comparison. Sometimes they are too fierce, sometimes too plain and sometimes they are girls like Sandra Mancini who get isolated from the herd.

There was barely a young buck at the Fratalanza who didn't wish to dance with this full-bodied girl, but only a few dared. They were afraid of becoming the butt for the jokes of their companions. As Darby's goddaughter she received a token respect from the elders of Little Italy. But amongst the younger ones she was still the outsider, still the scarlet woman.

It was her misfortune to have been born into a society devoted to the notion of the virgin bride. As Sandra had lost her virginity in such spectacular fashion, she was scarcely the type of girl the average Italian mother wished to see clinging to the arm of her favourite son.

A less proud spirit would have stopped coming to the dances long ago, because she sat so many of them out. Some of the other wallflowers would dance with one another and give the impression that this was what they preferred to do.

But Sandra wanted no part of such a subterfuge. So she sat by herself and developed a stone face. She would give no one the satisfaction of finding out how desperately she longed to dance.

It was her nineteenth birthday and she was wearing a dress of watered blue silk that Darby had given her that morning. She had fondly hoped that it might change her luck, but half the evening had already gone by without a single dance. It seemed a bad day on which to be alone.

She had been secretly praying that Angelo would come. He was the nearest thing to a friend she had in Little Italy, and with a fine disregard for the opinions of others would always dance with her.

She had almost given him up when suddenly she spotted him pushing his way through the crowd on the edge of the floor. He reached down and pulled her to her feet. "Come on, pal," he said, "we've got a lot of catching up to do."

They stayed on the floor for every dance and afterwards he walked her home. He stopped along the way and kissed her. "Happy birthday," he said, and slipped a ring on her middle finger.

She held it up towards the light. "What kind of a ring is it?" she asked.

"I don't know," said Angelo, "but it means you're my girl."

"Just like that?" she asked, smiling.

"Just like that!" said Angelo firmly.

16

CHARLIE ARTFUL

"Leave all these rascals behind. Take your family and settle down in Brighton before it's too late"
— Inspector Jack Capstick's advice to
Darby Sabini.

Darby Sabini was alone in the Eden Club. The other members had departed for their beds at midnight. Now, two hours later, Darby was still there, drinking slowly, very much at peace with his world. Darby, a man of habit, would drink ale until the stroke of midnight and coffee thereafter. "Black as night and sweet as sin," he'd say.

Now it was finally time to go. He had just started to turn out the lights when he heard a footstep on the landing.

"Hello, Jack," he said, not bothering to turn his head, "want some coffee?"

"Only reason I came," said Jack Capstick, taking a seat beside him at the bar. He was smiling, and with his ruddy complexion he looked more like a jolly farmer than a policeman.

"You know," he said, "you take too big a chance, drinking here alone at this time of night with the door open. Supposing it hadn't been me out there on the landing. Supposing it had been one of your enemies, say one of the Brummies. You'd have been dead before you'd even known he was there. Then he'd have walked away and dumped the gun in the river. As long as the man didn't talk, the perfect murder. No witnesses, no gun, and you with an army of enemies. What chance would we have of finding your murderer?"

Darby chuckled good-naturedly. "You've pounded too many beats, Jack," he said. "You walk like a copper. I heard your steps on the street outside. I heard them on the stairs and I saw you in the mirror there." He nodded towards the mirror behind the bar which gave a perfect view of the landing. "As long as I sit here, there's no need to turn my head. No one will surprise me."

"And no doubt you have that big gun of yours within reach of your hand?" said Capstick drily.

Darby shrugged and said nothing. There are some questions best left unanswered, even amongst friends. He broke the silence by saying, "And how about you, how safe do you feel walking the streets alone in the early hours? After all, there are a lot of villains who wouldn't weep at your funeral."

Capstick nodded soberly. "You're forgetting there's one essential difference between us. The police look after their own. If anything happened to me, there would be a blue army out there looking for my killer and God help him.

"Tell me, Darby, how many of your mob would go hunting for your killer? Massardo, Sewell, Gardini, Zoff maybe. But who else? How many real friends have you got?"

Darby considered the question gravely. "You've just named them," he said. "I've no illusions about the rest."

The underworld can have known few stranger friendships than this ... a friendship between the most powerful gangster of his day and a detective who had dedicated his life to hunting down villains.

Darby had many policemen in his pocket; but by some quirk of his nature he only liked the honest ones. Despite the mutual animosity, he respected Nutty Sharpe. But Capstick was the one he admired above all others. He was fond of saying that "every man, however moral he may be, has his price." Yet he never attempted to discover just what Capstick's price might be, because he felt that by so doing he would lose a friendship that he valued.

Capstick, for his part, had his own definition of villainy;

and the men he hunted were those who in turn preyed upon the weaker members of society. The muggers, the rapists, the pimps, the frighteners — these had always been his special targets. And he didn't look upon Darby as a criminal in that sense.

The story of how that hunt began had already become part of gangland legend.

Capstick had arrived as a police constable at Bow Street in the mid-twenties. And on his very first night on patrol in the tough Seven Dials area, he had been lured into a dark alley by three of the Titanics and beaten up. He had staggered back to the station, his face covered in blood and vowing vengeance.

Fate was kind to him. Just three weeks later, he was passing the Coach and Horses public house in the Strand when a disturbance broke out inside and men came tumbling into the street. He looked inside and spotted the three Titanics busy smashing bottles and putting the fear of God into the staff.

Capstick addressed the shaken landlord. "Leave these three to me," he said, drawing his truncheon. "Get everyone else outside and bolt the doors."

A crowd gathered on the pavement, listening to the sounds of battle from within and fearful that they were about to witness the demise of a police officer. Ten minutes went by before the doors opened again. The three Titanics emerged, bathed in blood.

Capstick, unscathed and cool as the proverbial cucumber, followed them, the truncheon still in his hand.

"All right," he said quite casually, "we'll walk to Bow Street, and the first one to get any other ideas can expect a tap from me."

And with that he marched the battered trio along the crowded Strand to Bow Street.

It was his way of informing the criminal fraternity that he'd arrived; and that from now on they had a new hunter on their patch. Following that day's work he became known as 'Johnny Wood', and in any rough-house his truncheon would become a fearsome weapon. As the years rolled by the underworld had given him another name, 'Charlie Artful', in recognition of the craft and cunning with which he pursued them.

Back in the Eden the two men had settled into a comfortable silence. Capstick was smoking his pipe, while Darby, a forty-a-day man, was lighting cigarette after cigarette.

Then Capstick said, "You know, Darby, there is nothing for you here. You've done what you set out to do. You've put a bit of backbone into the Italians, given them back their pride. Now all the tearaways are taking over, using your name, scaring good honest family men half to death. It's not your kind of game any more."

He paused. "Why don't you leave all these rascals behind? Take your family and settle down in Brighton before it's too late."

He knew that for Darby, Brighton had always possessed a certain glamour that he hadn't found in other seaside towns. He liked the big hotels looking out over the sea, the pier, the music halls and the racecourse up on the Downs.

The suggestion had taken Darby by surprise. "How could I spend my days in Brighton?" he asked. "All my friends are in London. There would be nothing to do."

Capstick smiled. "You wouldn't need to do anything special. Just lie on the beach. Have a garden. Grow roses."

He took great pride in his own rose garden, and invariably wore a rose in his buttonhole; but for the moment they meant very little to Darby, a man who'd never had a garden.

So he said equably, "I expect I will live in Brighton one day. But I'm too young for a while. You know, it's really a town for holiday-makers and old men."

They left it there and soon afterwards Capstick rose to leave. Darby turned out the lights, locked the door and left with him, saying drily, "If the streets are as dangerous as you say maybe we better protect one another."

And then as an afterthought, he asked, "Why did you really come to see me tonight?"

Charlie Artful smiled into the darkness. "It was raining outside," he said.

The night life of the Charmaine had changed Angelo even more than Darby had imagined it would. He had become as smooth and sophisticated as the millionaire playboys and the aristocrats who frequented the club.

Sometimes Darby worried about Angelo, wondered whether he'd made a mistake in giving him two women to protect, wondered whether by so doing he'd tamed his young tiger.

Much the same thought had crossed the devious mind of Max Foureux, leader of the French Mob and the latest of the protection racketeers to hit London's West End. The first two club-owners he'd approached had flatly turned him down, convinced that the traditional British mobsters would soon see off this upstart from Paris.

Both owners had been shot to death within the week. While those two murders were being committed Foureux was dining at the Savoy, something to which a score of witnesses could testify. The story spread like wildfire and there were no more arguments from unprotected club-owners. After all, how could you cope with a madman?

But it was the Charmaine with its rich and aristocratic guests that he considered the real prize to be won. He knew he was moving into rival territory, but having looked the club over he foresaw no great problems. A society queen such as Lady Diana would buckle at the first hint of violence, while that gigolo of a manager called Angelo was too pretty to hanker for the rough stuff.

Foureux was too experienced a campaigner to be misled entirely by appearances. He didn't doubt that there was a certain wiry strength concealed in the elegant frame of Angelo. Nor did he doubt that he had once possessed a certain toughness. How else would he have been given such a job? But he had watched him at work, seen the young matrons smiling at him with those bedroom eyes, seen the way he attended to Lady Diana's every need; and he understood how these things could happen. Constant exposure to this kind of life was bound to put a touch of softness into a man, however hard he might once have been.

He made a gentle approach to Lady Diana, was rebuffed, and so sent three big, burly fellows round to have a personal chat with Angelo. They arrived in the middle of a summer afternoon, two hours before the Charmaine was due to open, and found the dutiful Angelo alone in the bar. They pushed their way in uninvited, looking the place over silently and contemptuously in the manner of frighteners the world over.

Their leader stepped behind the bar, took down a bottle of vintage brandy, studied the label with seeming interest and then let it slip carelessly through his fingers. The bottle shattered on the stone floor and some of the brandy splashed on to the shoes of Angelo.

The three men studied the young manager's face and saw only a look of polite enquiry. Their leader spoke for the first time, his voice thick and guttural.

"Your lady boss," he said, "doesn't think she needs our help. We feel you should maybe tell her different before someone gets hurt." He thrust his head closer to that of Angelo, and his smile was full of cruelty. "Someone like you," he said.

Angelo raised his hands in surprise. "Maybe you should have come to me in the first place," he said. "Women don't always understand such things as this. Just tell me what you want and I'm sure we can come to some sort of understanding. We are after all men of the world. We don't need trouble. But first let me pour you a drink, then we can talk as friends. Isn't that the way it should be?"

It was the sort of speech that Darby might have made in a similar situation. However, it was spoilt by the weakness in Angelo's smile, by his too obvious eagerness to pacify three complete strangers who were threatening him. It was the kind of weakness that such men feed upon.

They ignored his offer of a drink and instead looked him over with open contempt, letting the silence drag out, forcing Angelo to be the first to speak again.

"All right," he said finally, "tell me how much you want to protect the Charmaine. I'm sure you're reasonable men and for my part I'd be glad to use you." He spoke so quietly that his voice was barely audible.

"How much do you take in a week?" asked the leader, puffing on a cigarette, beginning to enjoy the fear building up in his victim.

"I couldn't say offhand," said Angelo. "Maybe if you come back again at the same time tomorrow, it would give me a chance to work some figures out."

Angelo's hand was resting upon the bar top, and the leader let the hot ash from his cigarette fall upon the back of that hand and his smile grew crueller still as Angelo snatched the hand away.

"Try a little harder," he said. "Our boss is an impatient man who doesn't like to be kept waiting."

Angelo ran a nervous tongue across the knuckles of his singed hand. "The books are in the office," he said. "I'm not sure I should show them to you without asking Lady Diana first."

The leader of the trio gave him a shove so violent that it sent him staggering back into the shelves behind the bar and two more bottles crashed to the floor.

"Get moving," he growled. "As I was saying, our boss doesn't like to be kept waiting."

Without another word Angelo turned and led the way towards the office in the basement of the Charmaine. He walked the way a cowed dog walks, fearful of its next beating; and the three men exchanged quick, cruel grins.

They had already realised that there would be no need for violence, and yet they had decided to rough up this young popinjay just the same, simply for their personal pleasure.

Once inside the office Angelo began to place the account books upon the desk. He even dropped a couple in his eagerness to please. He reached into the desk once more and took out the last book.

"This is the one you need," he said, passing it to the leader with his left hand. His other hand held a gun which had been concealed in the desk for just such a purpose as this; and as the man accepted the book, Angelo clubbed him with stunning force above the left ear. He was unconscious even before he hit the floor.

It was a scenario that Carlo and Juan would have recognised all too well. The change in Angelo had been so sudden, so startling, that Foureux's two remaining frighteners had been slow to react. One of them made the mistake of rushing the young Sicilian, arms out as though to seize him in a wrestler's hold. He was struck full in the face with the gun butt for his pains. He too fell unconscious to the floor.

His companion immediately raised his hands high above his head, unnerved by the naked savagery in the face of Angelo.

"Keep those hands up," ordered Angelo, "turn around and face the wall, so I can search you. Move as much as your little finger and I'll shoot you down."

He had of course been playing the game he played so well. His voice like the rest of him had undergone the most remarkable transformation and was so confident, so chilling, that the man obeyed instantly.

But instead of searching him, Angelo used the clubbing gun again, this time against the base of the man's skull. Then working fast he bound the trio hand and foot, strapping their arms tightly behind their backs; and for good measure, gagging them too. And then, no longer in a hurry, he picked up the phone and rang Silvio Massarda.

When the receiver was lifted at the other end, he said, "This is Angelo. I need a closed van, not one of ours, at the back door of the Charmaine within half-an-hour. Can you manage or is that too fast for you?"

Massarda whose skill at stealing fast cars was legendary, chuckled broadly. "That's me," he said, "knocking at the door."

The leader of the trio was the first to regain consciousness, but Angelo was seemingly in no rush to conclude the affair. He waited patiently until all three were fully awake; and then taking his time, he shot them in each kneecap, quite oblivious to the muffled moans of agony.

He left the leader until last and before firing the two shots that would cripple him for life, he said, "Every time you limp, you'll remember me; but if you ever come looking for me again, I'll kill you. Even if we should meet by chance in some distant place, that will be your death warrant. You had better believe me."

And the man, looking into those eyes so calm, so confident, so cruel, believed.

With the help of Massarda, Angelo loaded the three men into the back of a florist's van; and then drove the van down to the country home of Foureux, followed by Massarda in a Bentley which belonged to the trio.

Angelo drove the van up the gravelled driveway and parked it in front of Foureux's Georgian doorway. They returned to London in the Bentley. And that night at the Charmaine, Angelo was once again his elegant, charming self.

17

A DREAM COMES TRUE

*"Is it so difficult for you to make up your mind?
Would you really be leaving so much behind? —
Silvio Massarda's marriage proposal.*

Even in her days of innocence, Anne Marlowe had never
really believed that James Frazer was in love with her. He
was too cold ever to know the true meaning of the word. She
had made do with his admiration and a certain fondness,
but now even those emotions had worn paper-thin. She
looked out of her bedroom window across the park, and
saw the grey sky and the drizzle which shrouded the distant
trees. This morning the world looked a very lonely place.
She was still standing there wrapped in gloomy thoughts
when the bell rang.

She opened the door to find Massarda standing there full
of smiles; and instantly her spirits lightened. He kissed her
gently and she slipped her arms around his neck and kissed
him back with the promise of early-morning passion that
surprised them both.

"Hey, hey!" cried Massarda, pretending to stagger. "A
fellow could get to like that kind of thing."

The truth was that fate had been kind to him. He couldn't
possibly have chosen a better moment to come calling. She
poured him a drink, and wanton thoughts were running
through her mind. She wanted him to take her in his arms
and make wild pagan love. But her life had been so chaste,
so uneventful for so long that she didn't even know how to
begin such an adventure. So she turned the conversation

back to more mundane matters.

"How did you know which door was mine?" she said.

"I asked the admiral down in the front hall," said Massarda. "He wanted to know if I was a friend of yours."

"So what did you tell him?"

Massarda shrugged. "The truth, naturally. I said you were my very best friend, the one and only." He paused. "I also told him that I had come to kidnap you, to take you away from all this. I don't think he believed me."

"You mean he doubted your word?" she said, beginning to laugh. The front-hall porter was one of the most humourless men she'd ever met. She could picture the scene with Massarda. She knew Frazer would have a full report of all this by nightfall. And she realised she didn't care any more.

"Hey," said Massarda, "don't you believe me either? I told you a long time ago that one day I would come to kidnap you and take you away for ever. Well, this is the day and I am the one."

"On a white charger?" she asked, still smiling.

Very gently Massarda took her face between the palms of his hands and turned her head so that she looked directly into his eyes.

"I mean it, Princess," he said. "I've come to take you away." To her astonishment she realised that he was deadly serious.

"And what are you planning to do with me once you've taken me away?" she asked, only half smiling now.

"Who wants to make plans for a lifetime? Isn't it better to live each day as it comes?" He smiled, and he was once more the Massarda she'd come to know. "Tonight I think I take you into my bed and make love right through the long night; wilder, more passionate love than anyone has ever made to you before; then tomorrow I make love through the long day. Unless, of course, you can think of a better plan."

He was in a strange mood, and with another man it could have been early-morning drinking. But with Massarda, it was money. There were two thousand pounds of Darby's money in his pocket which he was supposed to hand over to friendly police officers. He had already thought of a much better use for it.

Just like in the story books, he was going to make a dream come true … run away with his Princess and never be a gangster again. In his make-believe world there were no harsh realities. So he simply ignored the fact that Darby would have to come after him; and that the lady would in all probability say 'No'.

"Is it so difficult for you to make up your mind?" he asked gently. "Would you really be leaving so much behind?"

The words were cleverer than he realised. Long before he'd arrived that morning she'd asked herself the same question and given it a gloomy answer.

He was watching her face, practically reading her mind. "Who knows," he said, "I might even make you happy."

She let the silence drag out and then she smiled slightly. "You know," she said, "you're completely crazy; and so I think am I. Because I'm coming with you, if you really mean it."

Her own mood was as euphoric as Massarda's. She knew that if she went with him now the life she'd known would be gone for ever. There would be no more stardom. Frazer would see to that. And probably little more luxury either. But she just didn't seem to care. Now that the decision had been made, she was in a hurry to be gone. When Massarda asked her whether he could help her pack, she said quickly, "No, I want to leave it all behind. None of it's really mine anyway."

A few minutes later they went through the front hall arm in arm, past the astonished admiral. Massarda tipped him a wink as they went by. Halfway down Park Lane their laughter was swamped by the banshee wail of the Bugatti. They didn't once look back.

Georgie Sewell liked the rain; liked the feel of it, the sound of it, the smell of it. He parked his Buick coupé by the side entrance of Rose's Club and stood for a while with the collar of his blue suede jacket upturned, letting the rain beat against his face. By the force of a lifelong habit, he was studying the street. When finally satisfied, he went through that seldom-used side door, shaking the rain from his hat.

The bar was almost empty except for a few hustlers nursing their early-evening drinks. They looked him over quickly and just as quickly wrote him off. He nodded amiably enough at Rose Patrick and took his whisky and soda down to the far end of the bar where the lights were low; and Rose, wise in the ways of a violent world, made no attempt to join him. Her years as a gangland stripper had given her a nose for trouble.

The Cobblestone Fighter hadn't been inside her club for a year; and if he now wished to hug the shadows, there could only be one reason. He was waiting for someone and wished to be the first one to do the spotting. She even had a good idea who that someone might be.

Since their release from jail, Johnny and Mikey Williams had become regular and unwelcome visitors to the club. They had tried to put the protection bite on Rose and been given her scornful laughter in reply. But they had proceeded to underline the suggestion by first locking the doors and by then using their razors on one of the hustlers for no better reason than that she was there. Cutting people was still their pleasure, and they were still artists at their trade.

The hustler would never hustle again under the bright light. For her from now on, it would be the unlit shop doorways, the dark alleys; and if there were lamps in the streets where she plied for trade, she would take out the bulbs. After all, what kind of man would pay good money for a scarfaced girl? Johnny and Mikey had warned Rose that some lonely night, they would spend a little time with her. That is, unless she saw reason in the meanwhile.

Mikey had given her his evil grin. "That big body of yours," he'd said, "could do with a little carving. After we've finished, you'll only be half the girl you were." And he'd laughed at his own joke.

Ever since that night Rose had kept a loaded cosh on a shelf just below the level of the bar and within easy reach of her big right hand. But even so she felt uneasy on quiet, lonely nights such as this when rain washed the streets, locking her normal clientele in the warmth of their own homes. That was why she hoped the Cobblestone Fighter would stay a while. His threat to Mikey Williams was already a part of gangland legend.

She watched him from the corner of her eyes as he sat there nursing his drink, wrapped in some secret world of his own. And not for the first time she wondered where he found his pleasures. He had always treated her with an old-world politeness and yet he had always kept his distance, as though reluctant to put his trust in a woman. She knew that she had nothing to fear from him. She also knew that he was probably the most violent man she'd ever met, and this puzzled her.

Anne Marlowe was as nervous as any virgin bride. This had nothing to do with timidity or shyness or lack of sexual desire. No, she was nervous because she feared that she was about to become a terrible disappointment to Massarda; nervous because she sensed that, for both of them, reality could prove to be light-years distant from the dream.

She knew that tens of thousands of men had desired her. They had seen her in the bright lights of the Lyceum, wrapped in mink in the back seat of a chauffeur-driven Rolls, wandering through the nightlife of the city dressed in the most glamorous gowns, dripping in diamonds.

They had been so overwhelmed with her beauty that she became their fantasy lover. And each and every one of them imagined that a night of sex with Anne Marlowe would be the great unforgettable experience. But the truth was that any normal red-blooded housewife with an equally red-blooded husband knew more about the intricacies of love-making than she did. Frazer had been her one and only lover; and yet his cold heart made a mockery of both the word and the act.

She was that rare commodity, a heavily oversexed and beautiful lady of thirty who was still a mere novice at the game. She had yearned for so long to have a romantic lover such as Massarda; but now that the moment approached she was close to terror.

Massarda, still in the mood that would admit of no tomorrows, had taken the honeymoon suite in a luxury hotel on the outskirts of Brighton. The had shared their bottle of champagne and now, with the night before them, Massarda took her by the hand and led her to the bridal bed. He was surprised to feel her tremble, but he understood instantly and was delighted.

"Hey, Princess," he said, "with friends you can have no worries. That's all part of the world we left behind. Just relax and enjoy."

He inspected her with silent wonder in the moonlight. But refusing to be serious, he patted the flat plane of her stomach. "Who was that peasant who called you skinny?" he asked.

She reached for him but he pushed her back. "This first time," he said, "you do nothing. You just lay there and suffer. It's an old Italian custom. A most fearsome fate."

He had cleverly taken away her cause for concern. In this passive role her inexperience couldn't show through, and already she was undergoing sensations she'd never known before.

Somewhere around the dawn, lying in the crook of Massarda's arm, completely and utterly satisfied for the first time in her life, she smiled fondly at this strange man who had taken over her existence. She wondered whether she'd ever know another day as good as this. She was still wondering when she fell asleep.

At Rose's an hour had moved slowly by. Two more hustlers came in out of the rain, but no customers. And then at last the doors opened, and in walked Johnny and Mikey Williams and the beautiful Linden sisters who had confronted the Cobblestone Fighter on another day.

As ever they carried their handbags with the tools of the Williams's trade, the freshly sharpened razors, placed on top of everything else, ready to be produced at a moment's notice. They gave the hustlers a quick, contemptous glance and failed to recognise Georgie Sewell in the shadows. His head was down and he had the look of a solitary drinker with nowhere to go.

Mikey ordered two brandies and two double gins, and as Rose reached under the bar for the glasses, he looked down her cleavage with lustful eyes. The dress was cut daringly low even by Rose's standards; and for a good reason. It was good for business. Not for the first time he thought of all the things he would like to do to her; slow, cruel things that would keep her screaming through the long night.

He puffed his cigar until the tip was glowing red, and then suddenly stubbed it into her neck. Caught unawares, she gave a gasp of pain and then with a reflex action threw the brandy straight into the eyes of Mikey. He stepped back swearing violently, mopped his face with a grubby handkerchief; and then the first flush of anger went away to be replaced by pure pleasure. The time to hand out a long-overdue lesson had clearly come, and he could never hope to find a better night.

"Lock the doors, Johnny," he said, and turning to the hustlers, added, "you stay where you are, watch and learn what happens to whores who don't do what they're told."

He turned back to Rose. "You think you know what pain is, but you don't even know the meaning of the word. By the time we've finished with you, you'll be crying for your long-lost mother. But scream away. We like to hear you. On a night like this, nobody else will."

Johnny rammed the last bolt home and switched off the neon sign which had been blinking its message out on to the deserted streets. If any stray drinkers should walk by, they would assume that Rose had closed down the club for the night. He rejoined his brother at the bar and the sense of impending joy was on his face too — the kind of joy you see on the faces of men about to slide into bed for the first time with the woman of their dreams. Only with Mikey and Johnny, of course, the pleasures they had in mind were more primitive, more pagan than that.

It was then that Georgie Sewell stepped out of the shadows at last, smiling widely as though greeting two old friends who had been out of town for a while, as indeed they had.

"Need any help, Mikey?" he asked in that quiet voice of his. "She's a big girl for just two fellows to handle on their own. And anyway, isn't that what pals are for, to help out in times of trouble?"

For one terrible moment, panic had Rose by the throat. Then she realised that this was the mockery of a man who hated ponces beyond any other form of human cargo. And if there had been any remaining doubt in her mind, it was washed away when he said, "Been dreaming of me, Mikey?"

The shock in the eyes of Mikey answered that question more graphically than words could ever have done. Without taking their eyes off the Cobblestone Fighter, the two brothers reached out towards their womenfolk, palms upturned, waiting for the razors to be placed within their eager fingers; and for once their hands stayed empty. They remained in that position for a long moment, like a tableau on a stage, and then took a quick look to see what had gone wrong with a move that had never failed them before.

They were in time to see the Linden sisters in the grip of the hustlers who had watched this scene before, and vowed to carry out their own brand of vengeance on these men who had put their mark upon a colleague.

The Cobblestone Fighter was so relaxed that he was actually chuckling. "Looking for something, Mikey?" he asked and hooked him to the head in that selfsame moment. It was a deliberately muffled blow designed to weaken his man, but not to put him away.

He had always been vain about his appearance. He had tolerated the scars that traced their pattern across his face; but the gashes to his nose affronted his pride. Every time he looked into a mirror during the past three years he'd remembered Mikey, and waited impatiently for his return to the streets. Now he had the chance to repay the debt in full, and he was in no hurry at all.

He had almost forgotten Johnny, which could have been a fatal mistake. For as the first punch landed on his brother, Johnny had smashed his glass against the bar and raised the jagged edge. He was just about to plunge it into his enemy's face when Rose knocked him cold with her cosh, catching him expertly above the left ear.

After that it was never a fight. The Cobblestone Fighter gave his man a merciless beating, keeping him pinned against the bar. When he fell, he lifted him up again one-handed and was about to hit him with the other when Rose came round the bar.

"Let me," she said and placing her own broad back against the bar, she put her arms around Mikey and held him so that he became a human punchbag for the Cobblestone Fighter. Just before he finally lapsed into unconsciousness, Sewell spoke to him, spacing the words so that their meaning could never be misunderstood.

"If I ever hear you've been bothering Rose again," he said, "you're a dead man, Mikey. Even if she should be struck down by some bolt of lightning and you should be a hundred miles away at the time, I'll still come looking for you. So you'd better pray that she lives to be a very old lady."

Meanwhile the hustlers had been carrying out their own vengeance on the Linden sisters, first ripping away their fine clothes, and then beating them methodically with the high-heeled shoes which are part of the hustler's uniform.

They were beginning to lose interest when Johnny groaned and sat up. Instantly the girls transferred their attentions to him, and in this short space of time their entire personalities had changed. They were no longer the hunted, but the hunters; no longer the despised, but the despisers. They had reverted to some primitive tribal instinct more ancient than time itself.

The fear they'd felt for Mikey and Johnny had gone for

ever. Now, banded together, they felt invincible ... and as far as the Williamses were concerned, they probably were. A brawny pair of thighs descended upon Johnny's chest, effectively pinning him to the floor, and rough, anonymous hands began to tear at his clothing. His shirt came away in two pieces. One trouser-leg was ripped straight off; and suddenly fearful for his life, he began to plead for mercy. The girls' gleeful laughter gave him answer.

Georgie Sewell studied the scene in high good humour. He winked at Rose. "I think I'll go," he said. "It can only get worse."

Then, careful as ever, he added, "I'll leave by the side entrance. You better lock the door behind me, and whatever you do, don't switch on the sign."

He kissed her lightly, something he'd never done before, and stepped out into the rain.

He drove slowly through the darkened streets. In all his life, he had never felt more peaceful.

Darby was standing beside the bar in the Griffin and for once there was space all around him. The Sabinis, wise in the ways of their leader, sensed that he wanted it thus. He had just given the instruction that would send the razor teams in pursuit of Massarda, and he felt like a man who had put out a contract on his own son.

Of all the Italians, none had been closer to him than Massarda. Not Angelo, not even his own brothers. He knew that Massarda had never been a villain in the true sense of the word. A bit of a brigand, perhaps, but not a villain. He could be brave, foolhardy at times, but he wasn't really a violent man.

He had become a gangster simply because Darby was a gangster; and Massarda looked upon him as both friend and hero. If Darby had been a banker, Massarda would doubtless have been a banker too. Darby also understood about the money. He knew there was nothing personal in Massarda's act. In his world of make-believe he would have convinced himself that it wasn't Darby's money that he was running away with, but merely the money of dishonest policemen.

Again, he could understand the madness of Massarda's dream, the desire to change one's entire life-style with a single decision, to wash away the past and become an honest man overnight.

He could understand because he'd had similar dreams. He was already growing tired of gangland. He realised that Massarda would have based part of his plan on the hope that Darby would spare him, because Darby was his friend. And there was a terrible irony in such thinking.

For it was their friendship which prevented Darby turning the blind eye. He knew that the rest of the gang had been waiting and wondering; and that if he spared his long-time friend, the iron discipline of the Sabinis would be gone for ever. There could be no exceptions. The razor teams were already on the road.

Darby decided to go home for a rare early night. He left his drink untouched upon the bar.

18

THE PROMISE

"If I make a promise, I keep it. I always have and I always will. So I'm promising you that this man will never hurt you again. You have my word on that" — Scotch Yard's Jack Capstick, reassuring 'The Lady'.

Her real name was Mollie Smith, but in her chosen trade they called her 'The Lady' and for five years she had been the star of Scotch Eddie's band of whores. She had first seen the light of day in a Whitechapel tenement; but then, much in the manner of an Eliza Doolittle, she had acquired the trappings of an aristocratic world, learned to speak with a certain refinement, even developed a degree of eloquence that made her a rare and valuable commodity in the vice lands of Soho.

But that was yesterday. Today she was lying in a bed in Charing Cross Hospital, her face held together with seventy stitches, and even the morphine couldn't wash away the pain.

As the victim of a criminal assault, she had been placed in a room of her own with just one companion, the burly Jack Capstick with the inevitable red rose in his buttonhole. It was his fate to view the sundry cruelties of a cruel world. He had seen the bodies of murdered babes, the torture of innocent old men; but nothing had ever angered him more than the ruined face of Mollie Smith.

This wasn't just another case of razor-slashing. This was the sadistic trademark of a cold-hearted monster. Scotch Eddie was in some ways the counterpart of Jimmy Sabatini, the Clutching Hand. They were both artists at their trade;

and like all artists, they liked their work to be distinctive. However, there were two essential differences. Sabatini would never harm a woman, while for Scotch Eddie they were always the essential prey. Sabatini took pride in the speed of his hands. Scotch Eddie liked to take his time. Two of his henchmen would hold the girl tight, while he slowly carved her face ... placing a coiled serpent on one cheek and a matching replica on the other. Alongside the cruelty, there was arrogance. No girl yet had ever dared bear witness against him, and he was convinced that no one ever would. The fear he inspired was too great. And it was this contempt of the law which angered Capstick the most.

But none of this showed in his voice, which remained jovial as ever. "Come on, Mollie," he said. "It's no good closing your eyes and hoping I'll go away, because I won't. I'm a very patient man and I'll stay here all night if I have to."

When she remained silent, he shrugged and said, "If you won't talk to me, I'll talk to you. So just lay there and listen. I already know what happened and why. There are, after all, no secrets in Soho. You found yourself a rich client who offered to set you up in a flat of his own just so long as you became his exclusive property. And Eddie couldn't afford to let you do that. So he decided to teach you a very public lesson."

She started to shake her head. "Don't do that, Mollie," he said. "You'll only hurt your face and we'll be wasting each other's time. Everyone knows Eddie's trademark and you're wearing it. And unless I put him away, a lot of other girls will be wearing it too in the years ahead. I need your help to do that. At the moment you're in pain and you're too scared to help me, because you think Eddie will hunt you down and chiv you again. Oh yes, I know he's done that to other girls before. But you have my promise this won't happen. I'll protect you. I'll guarantee your safety."

The abused face of Mollie Smith took on an expression that might have been a scornful smile. "Now who's fooling who?" she said, and even now her voice was still that of a lady. "No policeman could protect me for ever; and that would be the only way."

Capstick smiled slightly, acknowledging the point. "Tell me," he said, "why do you find it so difficult to believe that Eddie could be made to feel an even greater fear than the one you're feeling now ... a fear so great that he wouldn't wish to be in the same city as you, let alone the same street?"

Again he waited for an answer, and when none came, he said patiently, "If I make a promise, I keep it. I always have and I always will. So I'm promising you that this man will never hurt you again. You have my word on that. I'm going to prove it to you, and when I do, I'll be expecting you to step into the box and witness against him."

Just before he left, this hunter of villains removed the rose from his buttonhole and placed it in a glass beside the bed. "Care for it," he said. "It's a living thing."

Later that day, Mollie Smith received another visitor, a man without a collar who took off his cap when he came into the room and whose teeth glinted when he smiled.

The young policeman who'd been ordered not to admit any strangers had clearly been expecting him; for he walked out into the corridor and left them alone. The newcomer took her hand in both of his and spoke quietly. Then he departed, having left a basket of English strawberries, something that Darby had always regarded as the ultimate delicacy.

Under the joint command of Lady Diana and Angelo, the Charmaine had become the flagship of the Sabinis' West End empire, a success symbol for all other clubs to follow. And much of the credit for this went to Angelo, whose Sicilian good looks charmed and intrigued some of the most sophisticated society women in town. Several of them had let him see the invitation in their eyes, and although he had always given them his most pleasant smile in return, he had never once made any attempt to pick up the offer. He preferred to let them think he was a little too naive to understand.

The truth was that older women had never appealed to him. He liked the lush young teenagers of Little Italy; and as he considered any woman in her mid-twenties to be past her peak, and any in their thirties as positively ancient, it wasn't too hard for him to shrug aside the temptations of the Charmaine.

He had been disturbed at first to discover that Lady Diana was also regarding him with what he would have described as bedroom eyes. But he had long ago decided that for her he would make the sacrifice. This was partly because he was a smart young fellow who had already learnt that in life it is often wise to play along with the whims of a boss. He remembered too the words of Darby when he had first sent him to the Charmaine.

"Go there, listen and learn," he'd said. "We won't always be racecourse toughs. Some day we will own places like this ourselves. And when that day comes we will need to understand that kind of world."

However, it wasn't entirely self-interest that had persuaded Angelo that he should be prepared to make the sacrifice. He had become genuinely fond of her, conscious of her loss, conscious of her lonelinesss. If a few stolen hours in her bed would make Lady Diana happy, then so be it. He had never been a chaser in the way that Massarda had been a chaser, but the Italian belles to whom he'd made love had all expressed their gratitude.

Despite that inborn streak of savagery, he was a warmhearted young man and it pleased him to know that one day soon he would be able to give her the kind of pleasures she had doubtless never known before. After all, he reasoned, she had come from a generation and a society stratum not noted for its wild passion.

But tonight alone with her, he was surprised to find himself for once a little ill at ease. In the past he had always been the pursuer, but now in the perfumed boudoir of this lonely lady the roles had somehow been reversed. In a bid to cover his unexpected confusion, he fetched a cloth to mop up a mere drop of champagne spilt upon the table top, and he double-checked that the wine had been correctly chilled. He was shocked to realise that she was laughing at him.

"My dear, you are very, very nice. But my word, you are tiresome at times. Here we are quite alone, both of us with that marvellous knowledge that we would be awfully good in bed together. And all you seem to want to do is wait on me hand and foot. Believe me, I have grown very tired of the bright young things who follow me around. Tonight I have decided to give myself a treat."

She paused, gentle mockery in her eyes. "That is, unless you really do decide to flee into the night. Otherwise I have the feeling that we're about to become very good friends indeed."

"I was going to say I don't really know anything about you," he said, and cursed himself silently as her delighted laughter rang out.

"Isn't that what a girl is supposed to say?" she asked. "No, all you need to know, my dear Angelo, is that I'm a wicked old woman with a ravenous taste for strong young men. So I choose not to simper and flirt, because men are terribly anxious to protect their pride and quite often never make the attempt for fear of failure. And life is awfully short, and each day it is shorter by one day. But in case you feel overwhelmed or anything, we don't have to make it definite. You can still cut and run and we can pretend it never happened."

She was well aware of the fact that in reality she had given him no choice at all. Young Sicilians such as Angelo could never allow themselves to run from anything, least of all a woman.

Angelo met her eyes, smiled and nodded, reassured by the knowledge that once they were between the sheets he would be the master in every sense, dominant partner and tutor too.

They proceeded to make love through the long night, and somewhere around the dawn, Angelo rolled over to his side of the bed and admitted that he was finished, utterly, completely and beyond recall.

She chuckled. "You do have to say something, you know. Some passing comment. I like to remember the better ones."

Angelo propped himself wearily on to an elbow and smiled at her, genuinely amused, and for the first time they really were friends. "Let's just say you're one very surprising lady."

She smiled at him fondly. "Could we also say that you're one rather surprised young man?"

There was no reply. His head had already slipped back on to the pillow and he was asleep. He awoke at midday to find her already dressed, bright-eyed and bushy-tailed.

She brought him a mug of steaming coffee and perched on the edge of the bed. "Tell me, Angelo," she said, "was that such a terrible chore?"

And seeing the puzzled look in his eyes, she added softly, "I mean having to make love to such an ancient lady."

He knew she was laughing at him, and this time he didn't mind at all.

Under Darby's kingship, Little Italy had enjoyed a period of peace which was quite unique in its history. The big gangs had discovered that raids on Sabini strongholds were doomed to failure. The rampaging bands of tearaways no longer dared to abuse the Italian women. And even the boys from Hoxton, who liked to pick a pocket or two, had learnt to behave like honest men once they'd crossed the frontiers of what was now known as Sabini land.

But one summer morning, this peace came under threat from an unlikely source. A crowd of old-style East End villains headed by those twin terrors, Dodger Mullins and Timmy Hayes, walked into the Yorkshire Grey, which as a Sabini stronghold ranked second only to the Griffin.

Hitherto, gangland battles had never been Dodger's style. Alongside Timmy Hayes, he had become a scavenger of the underworld. Both had discovered the advantages of owning a fearsome reputation. If they requested the loan of a tenner, no villain wise in their ways would ever quibble ... and such loans were of course never repaid. If they ordered a round of drinks and then discovered that their pockets were empty, barmen would simply chalk it down to experience. They had also been known to 'borrow' the wives of other villains — "just for company", they'd say — and the poor cuckolded husbands would more often than not accept the inevitable.

Even by the rough standards of the East End underworld, the senseless brutality of both Mullins and Hayes was extreme. Hayes, enraged at being asked to pay for his fish and chips, had picked up the shop-owner's cat and dropped it into a vat of boiling oil. And only a week earlier, Dodger had kicked a friendly pup to death with his hobnailed boots in Theobald's Road, claiming that "the little bugger barked at me." When a horrified passer-by pointed out that its tail had been wagging at the time, Dodger growled, "I don't see too well."

He was by no means devoid of courage. He had been decorated for bravery in the Kaiser's War and he had been a good street fighter in his day. But much of his courage nowadays took the form of bravado and this is what had happened today. While drinking in the Horns public house, he had described the Sabinis as a bunch of impostors and then gone marching into the Yorkshire Grey to prove the point, followed by his ragtail army.

Darby, hastily summoned from the Griffin, was feeling more aggravated than alarmed. He had no doubts concerning his soldiers' ability to handle Dodger's motley bunch of tearaways. But he didn't want trouble on his own patch, and took pride in his role as the peacemaker.

Today he surprised his followers by greeting Dodger like an old friend. The move surprised Dodger too, for there had been little love lost between them in days gone by. However, he ordered drinks all round, then drew this East End terror aside.

"Hasn't anyone told you," he said quietly, "that there's a contract on your life? The owner of the dog you killed the other day has offered the reward of a pony [twenty-five pounds] to the man who cuts your throat."

Dodger could barely credit his ears. "You mean some-one would have me murdered just for killing some pox-ridden mongrel?"

Darby shrugged. "Dogs mean nothing to me," he said, "but apparently the man's young daughter had a certain fondness for the animal, and so the man has taken it personally."

Dodger wasn't to be intimidated that easily. "I'll stand and fight any man face to face in a fair fight," he said.

Darby doubted whether the Dodger had ever been engaged in a fair fight in his entire lifetime, but he didn't say so. Instead he said, "I know, old friend, that like me you enjoyed the rough and tumbles. But those days have gone. Some of these young bucks just off the boats from Italy think nothing of cutting a man's throat. To them, it's all in a day's work."

At that moment, Nino and a ferocious-looking band of young Italians walked into the bar and began to view Dodger with some interest. A few minutes later an argument broke out between them which was eventually quelled by Nino.

A more astute man than the Dodger might have suspected by now that a little charade was being played out for his benefit, but intelligence had never been one of his major qualities.

Darby summoned Nino to his table. "What was all that about?" he asked.

Nino hesitated before answering and said briefly, "Just a dispute over money," and then bending down, he whispered in Darby's ear.

Darby, at his most ingenuous, said out loud, "You mean a dispute about who earns the pony?"

Most of Dodger's lukewarm supporters, alarmed by the growing army of Sabini soldiers, had by now left the bar, and he was feeling increasingly isolated.

"Tell me," he asked Nino, "would you really cut a man's

throat for a pony?"

Nino studied Dodger's throat for a long moment, considering the question. And then he said matter-of-factly, "Not in my best suit. It can be a messy business."

With that Nino returned to the warlike band beside the bar and Darby watched him go, shaking his head in mock sorrow. "I don't know what the world's coming to," he said. "These young fellows will be the death of us all. But take my advice, old friend, stay away from Little Italy for a while. I'll let the man's temper cool and then I'll talk to him, maybe buy a new dog for his daughter. And then, who knows, maybe he'll lose his taste for vengeance."

As a gesture of good faith, Darby and some of the older Sabinis accompanied Dodger Mullins and Timmy Hayes through the streets until they were well clear of Little Italy. An ignominious retreat for men of such warlike persuasions.

Men achieve popularity in sundry ways. Some achieve it with generosity, by the goodness of their hearts or through their friendly dispositions. Others achieve it with their fame, their sporting prowess or by heroic deeds.

But Scotch Eddie, running true to form, bought his through the enforced generosity of others. His shady ladies, with little choice in the matter, would offer cut-price rates to his fellow-villains. At gangland stag nights, the strippers wouldn't be paid at all. And he would put on special shows for those with depraved tastes, of which there were many within the ranks of the ungodly.

All of which helps to explain why he was standing at the bar of the Continental in Compton Street, a gangster haunt, looking like the most popular man in town. But the latest arrival, Jack Capstick, didn't appear to share that opinion. Pushing his way across the crowded floor, he went up to the popular one and said, "I'm taking you in, Eddie."

Eddie was so confident that he actually laughed out loud. "Why, if it isn't Charlie Artful himself," he said, playing to the gallery. "What charge would it be this time?"

Just for once Capstick wasn't smiling. "How about grievous bodily harm or wounding with intent for starters?" he said. "I'll probably think up some more on the way to the station."

But men like Scotch Eddie make a point of knowing the law rather well. "Have you got a warrant?" he asked, and when Capstick didn't bother to reply, he said, "I'm betting you haven't and as you're on private property, I have every right to resist arrest. After all, you'd be the one breaking the law, not me; so I know my pals here will protect me."

At this, there was a chorus of assent; and Eddie was amazed that a man as streetwise as Capstick should have made such an elementary mistake. A lot of young policemen had made that same error around Soho and been badly beaten as a result. But this man was reputed to be in a league of his own.

However, Capstick showed no signs of backing down. "It's your choice, Eddie," he said. "You come in the easy way or you can come in the hard way. It's up to you."

The mob had already blocked his path towards Scotch Eddie. Now they moved menacingly towards the lone policeman and, as if by magic, a truncheon appeared in Capstick's hand. He was once more 'Johnny Wood'; but the odds were still stacked heavily against him.

And then, with perfect timing, the door opened and Darby Sabini stepped into the room flanked by Georgie Sewell, Bert Marsh and George Thomas ... four men who had all made their reputations in the ring. They drove forward like the professionals they were, barely wasting a punch, and their rivals were falling like ninepins. The main fight was over before it had barely begun. And Capstick, armed with his favourite weapon, had proved to be equally quick, equally effective. His first blow had cracked Eddie's collarbone; and then forehand and backhand, the truncheon had smashed against the cheekbones of the whoremaster.

They took him outside and Darby spoke to him quietly before his friend, this hunter of villains, marched him away.

"You're going inside, Eddie," he said, "for a long time; and on the day you come out, we'll be waiting for you at the doors of the jail. We're going to put you on a train to Glasgow and that's where you'll stay. If you ever come back to London, even for a day, you're a dead man. You'd better remember that."

Just for once Jack Capstick was a man devoid of mercy. He took Scotch Eddie along a carefully chosen route to Vine Street police station ... along Old Compton Street, Brewer Street and into Piccadilly Circus itself, knowing that there would be prostitutes in every doorway. He wanted them to witness the downfall of a whoremaster who had once spread terror in their ranks.

Eddie had taken such a beating that he could barely walk; yet each time he stumbled Capstick would prod him with that deadly truncheon. "Come on, Eddie," he'd say, outwardly the jovial farmer, "pick your feet up. You can do better than that, I know."

Some of the girls left their beats and formed a procession, cat-calling and jeering. By the time they reached Piccadilly, the procession had become a mob, and this most unusual policeman did nothing to discourage them. He was still remembering the ruined face of Mollie Smith.

Scotch Eddie went through the doors of Savile Row as if into a haven. On another day, Capstick had marched three prisoners along the Strand to give his own message to the underworld at large. Today's message had been designed for the men he despised most of all, the pimps and the ponces.

He was pleased with his night's work. Thanks to the help of a gangster chief, he had kept a promise the only way he knew how.

19

THE BOBBED-HAIRED BANDIT

*"I know you were my friend and I know I let you
down. But can't you look me in the face and say
you understand?"* — *Silvio Massarda's appeal to
Darby Sabini*

The denizens of the Griffin had seen more than their fair
share of drama. They had twice witnessed the downfall of
the Trimmer. They had heard the roar of guns and glimpsed
the wicked flash of knives. On more tranquil nights, they
had listened to Darby's rendering of 'Rosie Magoola.' But
they had never fallen quite so silent as this before. One by
one, they turned to look at the door and still no one spoke
a single word. Darby was the last to turn, and it was almost
as though he'd known all along who would be standing
there. But even so he had the look of a man who'd just seen
a ghost.

Silvio Massarda was standing just inside the door, but he
was a far cry from the happy-go-lucky companion of days
gone by. He had been slashed from ear to ear, and the scars
were still red and raw. His face had been sewn together by
an amateur, giving it a grotesque appearance. He smiled,
and was unaware that the smile came through as a scowl.

There were men there who had helped to put those
terrible scars upon his face; hard, cruel men who'd enjoyed
their butchery. Today even they couldn't bear to study their
handiwork. Massarda began to walk towards the bar and
men moved aside hastily to let him through. He had never
been a truly violent man, but he'd carried a gun and used
it on occasions. Was he now about to use that gun on

Darby, the man who'd sent the razor teams after him?

Darby had turned away and was studying the whisky in his glass as though it occupied all his thoughts. However, he could see Massarda in the mirror behind the bar, and like everyone else he was wondering why he'd come. He had always prided himself upon being able to read the minds of his fellow-men, but how could you read the mind of a man through a face such as this?

Massarda came to stand beside Darby, but the gold-toothed commander continued to stare into his glass. He was half expecting violence, certainly anger, and so Massarda's first words surprised him.

"Can you forgive me?" he asked.

Just for once in his life Darby was unable to find the words he wanted, so he stayed silent; and Massarda misunderstood this too.

"I know you were my friend and I know I let you down. But can't you look me in the face and say you understand?"

Darby was too well aware of the fact that everyone in the bar was waiting for his answer; and because he had no wish to betray his true feelings, he asked a question of his own.

"Are you saying that you want to come back?"

"No, I've said all I came to say," replied Massarda, and with that he turned and walked out of the bar.

Silvio Massarda had played a key part in Darby's life and now he missed him. Primarily he missed him as a friend and companion. Massarda had always seen the lighter side of life; and Darby had often wished that he could view the world through the eyes of his lieutenant.

He also missed him for his talents. For well over a decade, Massarda had been the Sabinis' top getaway driver. He'd had a rare gift with cars, had loved them the way he loved women and handled them with much the same finesse.

His red Bugatti had seldom been used on raids as it was too easily recognised. "Once seen, never forgotten," boasted Massarda. So on the day of a raid he'd steal a car in the morning, tune it up in the afternoon and use it as a getaway car late that night. But as a lover of cars, he had one idiosyncrasy. Instead of dumping cars in faraway places as most thieves would have done, he liked to leave them as near their home as he dared.

Several owners had been pleasantly surprised to find their cars running better than ever before.

But now, due to a twist of fate, Darby badly needed a driver of Massarda's calibre and there was just no one in the ranks who measured up. A lone Sabini van had been rammed and hijacked on its way home from Royal Ascot and something in the region of £12,000 had been taken. Darby blamed himself. In the past, these vans had always been part of a Sabini cavalcade and as such well guarded. But the gang's supremacy and the prevailing peace had lulled Darby into a false sense of security and this had come as a rude awakening.

Through his matchless underworld sources, he already knew that the hijackers were part of the Upton Park Mob, a predominantly Jewish gang which operated in the West Ham area of East London. In fact, they weren't making any real attempt to keep their coup a secret. Successful hits on the all-powerful Sabinis were, after all, something to boast about.

So Darby decided to carry out his own raid on the Upton Park's proudest possession, an exclusive gambling club known as the Willows and situated in a lonely spot on the Essex marshes. He didn't look upon the proposed raid with any enthusiasm, for he had never been happy when operating beyond the bounds of London.

The city was home to Darby, its narrow streets and alleyways all comforting avenues of escape whenever the need arose. Out on the country roads, he felt vulnerable. Smash and grab was not his speciality. He needed help, and just for once didn't know where to turn.

Georgie Sewell solved the problem by bringing his friend Ruby Sparks to the Eden late one night. Ruby, labelled by the newspapers of the day 'the King of Smash and Grab', was a villain much after Darby's heart. A man who used intelligence and controlled daring and who, like Darby, abhorred mindless violence. He was powerfully built, conservatively dressed and very relaxed. A mature version of Massarda; for he, too, refused to take the world seriously. The choice of the name 'Ruby' gives some clue to his character; for this was the reminder of a gaffe that many villains might have preferred to forget. As a cat burglar, he had robbed a house in Park Lane and pocketed a box of red stones. A receiver had told him that they were worthless. So he gave them away, only to discover next day that the stones belonged to a maharajah and were worth £40,000.

Darby suggested a joint venture with "everything we take split down the middle", and then added modestly, "Of course in such matters we're amateurs compared to you."

Ruby chuckled. "Some amateurs!" he said.

But Darby persisted. "In such matters as this, that's what we are. Every man has his speciality. We understand the racecourses, how to protect the clubs, how to raid the small-time spielers of our enemies. But this is different. This is a big country club quite possibly protected by the local police. That's why we need you to guide us."

Ruby nodded equably. "In that case," he said, suddenly all business, "let's keep it simple. The banks are closed on a Saturday, so that's when the safes will be full. A club such as the Willows will probably close around two o'clock in the morning — I'll check that out. But this is the time for us to go in, when the last guests have gone and the staff are tired and not so alert as usual.

"I'll get a lay-out of the place, discover where the money's kept; and we'll aim to get in and get out again without being spotted. However, we may not be that lucky, so we make sure we cover everything that could possibly go wrong. We have to reckon that some of the staff will be honest men, and honest men talk. Clubs such as this don't hire croupiers with criminal records, otherwise they soon lose their licences. Therefore we'll need to wear masks or at least scarves over our faces."

Darby seemed immensely impressed. "How many men do you need?" was all he asked.

"You and Georgie plus six good fighting-men," said Ruby, "just in case things go wrong. I'll supply the car and a van." Then, seeing the puzzled look on Darby's face, he added, "The Upton Park crew should know a thing or two about peters; so we may need to bring it back with us. That's why I want a van."

"How about the drivers?" asked the Cobblestone Fighter, who was clearly looking forward to the night to come. Life had been too quiet for his liking of late.

"I'll use my own," said Ruby firmly. "I always use the best."

On the appointed night, at Ruby's insistence, they met the Mercedes on the outskirts of town at Chingford and it was easy to see the reason why. Both the front and rear bumpers had been adapted smash-and-grab style into ramrods — something that the dullest of policemen would have spotted on a brightly lit city street.

Ruby climbed into the passenger seat beside the driver. Darby, Nino and Sewell sat in the back. The driver, wearing a red motoring coat with high upturned collar and a red beret, handled the big car beautifully; and the first part of the plan worked like a charm.

The Willows was situated on private land, and they went in through an unmanned gate. The driver switched off the engine a hundred yards short of the club, and they coasted into the shadows down the side of the building, with merely the whisper of tyres.

They crept up the back stairs undetected, and opened the office door to be confronted by a lone floor manager, who looked positively terrified at the sight of Darby's gun. He put up no resistance as he was swiftly bound and gagged. The safe, as Ruby had predicted, was too tough to crack instantly; so they carried it down the stairs and into the van.

They drove away quietly and were just about to congratulate themselves on a near-perfect job when their luck ran out. An alarm bell began to ring and the gate closed, cutting off their escape route. Back at the club, Upton Park mobsters had been clambering into cars, and now two cars were setting off in pursuit.

The driver of the Mercedes didn't hesitate. The accelerator pedal was pressed flat against the boards and the big car surged forward with an awesome roar, smashing the gate to smithereens. The van, vulnerable due to its lack of speed, was waved past. Then Ruby's driver executed a handbrake turn, spinning the car through 180°, and now they were running back the way they'd come, effectively blocking the road, giving the van time to escape.

The Upton cars were coming towards them in single file but slowing … their drivers for the moment puzzled and uncertain. For the Mercedes was heading straight for the lead car, lights blazing and gathering speed. At the very last moment, when a head-on crash seemed inevitable, the lead driver's nerve broke. He braked fiercely, swerved off the road to the left and was promptly rammed by the car behind.

Ruby's driver skimmed past the two of them and made the skimming look easy. Then another handbrake turn had the car spinning, and within seconds they were once more driving through the shattered gate and disappearing into the night. A couple of shots rang out and a bullet ricocheted harmlessly off a rear wing.

Ruby patted the driver's shoulder and said to Darby, "Didn't I tell you, I always use the best?"

The driver chuckled and spoke for the very first time, saying, "You could have said the *very* best."

It was a woman's voice, and Darby unsurprised said drily, "The Bobbed-Haired Bandit', I presume."

In the unlit interior of the Mercedes, she had been partly disguised by the high collar of her coat and the beret; but Darby had guessed her identity soon after they'd left Chingford. It was her silence which had given her away. In Darby's experience, men setting out on potentially dangerous ventures such as this tended to talk freely in a bid to ease the tension.

He had guessed the reason for that silence too. Ruby would have been well aware of Darby's reluctance to use women in perilous situations ... even a woman such as Lilian Goldstein, the Bobbed-Haired Bandit, one of the most romantic robbers in the annals of crime.

The *Daily Express* had given her the tag with a headline which ran: 'YARD HUNT FOR THE BOBBED-HAIRED BANDIT.'

The story ran: "A girl bandit with dark bobbed-hair, a small innocent-looking face and an active and intelligent brain is being sought by Scotland Yard and other police authorities. She is often dressed in a red beret and motoring coat of the same colour, or in an all-green motoring outfit, and she is believed to be the 'brains' behind recent country-house raids which have resulted in losses running into several thousands of pounds. In these instances she has acted as the chauffeur of a car — usually stolen — while her male companion has actually carried out the robbery."

The story failed to mention that the male companion was invariably Ruby Sparks, who was hopelessly in love with the lady.

Fleet Street came up with sundry theories about this mysterious motor bandit. According to some, she was a society woman seeking a new thrill. Others pictured her as a lady racing driver, while one somewhat quaintly put forward the notion that she was a member of a famous (though unnamed) symphony orchestra ... and at the close of a concert she would demurely take her bow, put her violin in its case, slip on her driving gloves and set off on yet another daring heist.

Nutty Sharpe, one of her chief pursuers, knew her identity but was never able to catch her. And even that dyed-in-the-wool copper admitted a grudging respect for both her talents and her courage.

For a man who had just been involved in a successful coup, Darby was in a surprisingly sombre mood, and barely spoke again on the journey back to London. He had hoped that this raid on the Willows would forge a permanent link with Ruby; but now he knew he could never use him again.

The following night in the Eden, he explained his reasons to the Cobblestone Fighter. "They work as a team," he said. "Ruby will never work without her; and I will never work with her. We've never used women yet and I'm not about to start now."

Just for once the boss and his lieutenant weren't in accord. Sewell had wanted his friend Ruby alongside him, and he made no attempt to hide his disappointment.

"Everyone uses women nowadays. Lizzie Chandler has as much say in the running of the Titanics as Bargee himself. The Forty Thieves are all women and the Elephant Mob would be lost without them. So why do we have to be different?"

Darby shook his head. "No one is going to shoot the Forty Thieves. If they get caught, they'll spend a few weeks in Holloway, meeting old friends. But one of these days, Lilian will meet a driver who doesn't lose his nerve at the last moment or someone who shoots straight, unlike those impostors last night."

"That's a chance she's taking all the time," Sewell pointed out reasonably enough, "and one she'll keep on taking. At least with us, she'd have a team behind her."

"Maybe," said Darby stubbornly, "but I don't want to be the one to bury her."

Sewell tried one last tack. "Ruby is in love with Lilian, and if anything happened to her, he'd be heartbroken. But he accepts her the way she is and doesn't try to change her. So why can't we accept her too?"

"I know the way Ruby feels about her," said Darby, genuinely puzzled, "and that's why I don't understand him." Then he added, "Maybe I'm just an old-fashioned man."

"Maybe you are at that," said the Cobblestone Fighter, no way pleased.

20

RED MAX

"It's a case of be careful or be dead. That one's buried a few in his time" — Sabini soldier Johnny Cattini speaking about white-slave trafficker Emile Allard

Georgie Sewell was sitting at a corner table in the Charmaine, listening to the club's resident singer Peggy-Sue. She was singing 'Moon River,' his favourite song. Music moved him the way nothing else could.

He had cases filled with records; and in his bachelor days, he would listen to these right through the long, lonely nights. Always the vocalist would be a woman, and this was a strange thing; for he had never really liked women. He had considered them shallow. And that stone face which could put such fear into the hearts of his fellow-mortals had for him proved to be the true barrier between the sexes.

Then came the day when a girl called Hetty looked into that forbidding face and glimpsed something that no one else had seen before. And it was in her company that for the first time in his life he came to know the meaning of love and tenderness.

The transformation hadn't been total. He was still not a sentimental man and it was only at times like this, when he listened to soft music, that he realised just how much she'd changed him. Behind that fearsome façade, there were emotions that would have astonished many of those who thought they knew him well. He was capable of introspection. He understood his own dark nature, and sometimes he wished that his heart hadn't stayed quite so cold. He had often envied other men's capacity for love. But then, having seen the pain such love could cause, he'd decided that he was perhaps better the way he was.

Yet tonight, maybe because the music had softened his mood, his gaze kept straying to a twelve-year-old girl with blonde hair and cornflower-blue eyes. He knew she was twelve, because this was her birthday and there was a cake with twelve candles. The table had been placed on the normally empty dance floor, so that she would be close to the stage.

Her mother sat on one side of her and a man called Emile Allard on the other; and it was the presence of Allard that disturbed the Cobblestone Fighter. Here was a man known variously as Max Kassel, Emerald, Washman, Red Max, Max the Red, Ginger Max and Max le Rouquin. He was officially a diamond merchant, but this was simply a cover. He had been a partner of Micheletti the Assassin, and he now controlled that infamous empire.

So just what could such a man as this be doing, acting as a doting father? Sewell had never really liked other people's children. He loved his own sons with a fierce pride, although he'd never told them so. But the other children of the world meant little to him. However, there was something about this young girl that appealed to him: the delight on her face, the way she laughed.

Peggy-Sue had spotted her immediately, and when the diners asked for an encore, she turned to the girl and said, "Honey, it's your night. What would you like me to sing?"

Surprisingly the girl had asked for 'Alice Blue Gown.' Intrigued, Peggy-Sue had smiled. "Sure I will; but first tell me why you like that particular song." And the girl had said, "Because it's my mother's favourite."

When the song had been sung, the girl without any prompting had taken the single red rose from the table, run forward and handed it to Peggy-Sue. And although Peggy-Sue had tried to give it back, the girl had insisted. "No," she had said, "I want you to keep it."

Such generosity on such a day astonished the Cobble-

Chief Inspector Frederick Dew Sharpe of Scotland Yard. "Known to the underworld as 'Nutty' Sharpe and to the newspapers as 'the man who never forgot a face'"

Red Max Kassell alias Emile Allard, czar of the white slave traffickers. "Do such men really deserve to live?" asked Darby Sabini

Ruby Sparks. "He was hopelessly in love with the Bobbed-Haired Bandit"

Alberto Dimeo alias Albert Dimes. "He followed Darby's star"

stone Fighter. He remembered his own youthful birthdays. His presents had been few and far between; and if anyone had so much as cast acquisitive eyes, the hairs would have risen on his neck...

Red Max was being equally generous, ordering the very best champagne in the house, the most expensive box of chocolates; and then producing a diamond necklace which glittered in the lights.

Sewell summoned Johnny Cattini to his table.

"See those people at that table on the dance floor? When they leave I want them followed. Once they've settled in for the night, ring me. It doesn't matter how late. I'll be waiting."

Cattini was the best shadower in the Sabini gang. Darby had once said, "Cattini could follow a man across a desert and the fellow would never know."

Even so, Sewell warned, "Be careful. He's a sly one." Cattini surprised him by chuckling, "It's a case of be careful or be dead. That one's buried a few in his time."

It was an open secret that Red Max had been a suspect in several murder cases, and all the victims had a common link. They were all former associates who knew too much about his white-slave activities. Josephine Martin, known as 'French Fifi', had been strangled with one of her own silk stockings in her Archer Street flat; while another partner, Martial le Chevalier, had been stabbed to death in a particularly brutal fashion.

Anne Marlowe's life had undergone a sea change. She had moved from her luxury Mayfair apartment to a modest two-room flat in Hove. The minks and the diamonds lay in the past and so did the fame. Neighbours looked upon her purely as the wife of a scar-faced man.

She had exchanged a cold-hearted millionaire for a warm-hearted pauper. The two thousand pounds had been spent in spectacular fashion; and it was only after it had gone that Massarda confessed it was all he had in the world. Even so, she would have been content enough with this new life if it hadn't been for the intense despair which she sensed in her lover.

The men who had come with their razors in the night had done more than wound his face. They had wounded his pride. All the laughter had gone away from Massarda, and try as she might she couldn't make him happy. Sometimes in the middle of the night he would become the carefree lover of old; but this was only because the lights were out. Despair would return with each new day.

Hitherto she had never really hated a man, but she hated Darby now with every fibre of her being. She had never seen so much as a picture of him; and yet when he came calling at her door, she recognised him instantly. He had taken his cap off, and she had no means of knowing that this was the man's way of showing respect.

It had required more courage than Darby cared to admit to make the journey, and the embarrassment showed through. She had no wish to put him at his ease.

"Silvio is out for the day," she said, and added bluntly, "There is no point in waiting. You would be the last man he'd wish to see."

"I know he's out," said Darby in that quiet voice of his. "You were the one I came to see."

And with that he stepped through the doorway as though invited and moved into the lounge. He looked around and nodded in approval. He was not a neat man himself, but he admired neatness in others.

"How is he?" he asked. "I don't mean his face. That will heal. I mean, what kind of a man is he now?"

She wanted to hurt him more desperately than she had ever hurt anyone. "What we should be asking," she said, "is what kind of a man are you? Ever since I've known Silvio he's talked about you. You were both his hero and his friend. I think he loved you more than he can ever love me.

"So what do you do? As soon as he has his first chance of real happiness you send men who are no better than animals to cut him and scar him for life. Even then it wasn't the pain or the look of his face in the mirror that destroyed him. It was the knowledge that you were the one who sent them. And you have the gall to stand there and ask me what kind of a man Silvio is now. You know as well as I do that he's a broken man, because you broke him."

It wasn't often that Darby attempted to justify his actions to strangers, but he tried now. "If it had just been the two of us, Silvio and I," he said, "he could have had the money and I wouldn't have lifted a finger.

"He wouldn't have been my friend any more; but that's all that would have happened. However, this wasn't my money. It was Sabini money and these are my people. Silvio knew the rules. He gave me no choice. If there had been any other path open to me, I would have taken it."

His patience only angered her the more. "Silvio called you an honest man and a brave one. Do honest men use razors upon their friends? Do brave men have to send others to do that kind of work for them?"

Darby sighed and his manner became firmer, more authoritative. "I don't expect you to like me," he said, "but don't let your pride stand in the way of your man's happiness. I have a small nightclub in the south of France." He grimaced in self-parody. "Something for my old age. I want him to have it and I want you to help him. You understand how such places are run. There are good doctors over there who can mend his face for him and in time he'll become the man you first knew."

He took out a wad of notes and tossed it carelessly upon the table. "There's five thousand there. You look after it for him. He was never any good with money."

She was still wary. "What terrible deed," she asked, "does he have to do in return for all this?"

He surprised her by smiling, genuinely amused by her suspicions. "You'll make him a good wife," he said. He paused and added soberly, "I thought you would leave him. That's why I came. I was going to ask you to change your mind, to give you the money so that you'd stay. Now I can see I don't need to ask. I wouldn't wish to insult you."

"Supposing Silvio doesn't wish to accept this from you?"

Her voice was curious, with much of the antagonism gone.

"Tell him I came to ask this as a favour," said Darby. "Tell him that one day I may need a new base when London becomes too warm for me. Tell him that. He'll never refuse me a favour."

She still didn't like him, but she didn't hate him either. "You're a strange man," she said. "Tell me, why are you really doing this?"

"Put it this way," said Darby. "I don't want to look at his face ever again." He wasn't smiling.

Allard left the Charmaine in his chauffeur-driven Daimler, sitting in the back seat between the girl with the cornflower blue eyes and her mother. They had no reason to believe that they would be followed, and so Cattini trailed them without any trouble to the vice czar's elegant house in James Street, a turning just off Oxford Street.

He watched as Allard ushered mother and daughter into his home. The chauffeur remained in the Daimler and ten minutes later the mother, this time alone, climbed into the car and was driven away. Cattini made no attempt to follow them. His interest lay in the house.

He parked his own car, a nondescript Humber, a few doors away and settled down for what he sensed would be a lengthy vigil. He had the ability to hover in the limbo between waking and sleeping, to be totally relaxed and yet never miss a beat. That's the way he went through the long night.

At ten o'clock the following morning, the mother returned in the Daimler and went into the house. Within a few minutes, the front door reopened. Allard and the mother emerged with the daughter between them, no longer the carefree happy girl of the night before. She was walking on legs as tottery as those of a new-born foal and without her mother's supporting hands might well have fallen.

Cattini was one of the hard men of the Sabini regime. He would carve his mark on the face of a rival gangster without a qualm or a moment's regret. Yet the sight of this young girl horrified him.

He watched as they helped her into the Daimler. There was a brief conversation between Allard and the mother which ended when he slipped a wad of notes into her handbag. The mother then joined her daughter in the car. Just before the Daimler pulled away from the kerb, Cattini drove past and then allowed himself to be overtaken before he reached the end of James Street: an old shadower's trick he had learnt many moons ago. He then shadowed the Daimler to a modest house in Peckham, clearly home for mother and daughter, and then headed for the Griffin.

Darby listened to Georgie Sewell's report with a grave face, grimacing with distaste when he heard about the girl spending the night in Red Max's house. But the story only confirmed what he already knew. Allard had a taste for the very young ... a taste that affected both his personal and business lives. Many of his girls who went so hopefully to faraway places were still in their teens, and many of those lured into his bed were below the legal age.

"Does such a man really deserve to live?" he asked the Cobblestone Fighter.

Considering the question barely worthy of an answer, Sewell asked a question of his own. "Shall I call on this ponce and have a little talk?" At that moment, he was picturing the girl's face in the Charmaine.

Darby, who had come to read his lieutenant's mind rather well, was tempted to unleash his tiger. He knew that he would never kill by intent. He also knew that when passion was involved, those terrible hands could so easily hammer a man to death. So, reluctantly, he shook his head.

"We'll light the kindling wood and fan the flames," he said. "After all, why risk a hanging for a monster such as this?"

He had decided to use the same tactics as those he'd used to destroy Castanar and Micheletti; and he had been encouraged in this by another quotation learnt from Alf White: "Those whom the gods wish to destroy, they first drive mad."

It had been easy enough to set Castanar against Micheletti the Assassin; and it proved equally simple to fan the flames of an existing feud between Allard and another white-slave trafficker, Marcel Vernon, known in England as George Edward Lacroix.

Both ran international empires and both were on the run from police in other countries. Before coming to England, Red Max had fled from Buenos Aires and then from Paris. Vernon had escaped from Devil's Island and made Soho the base of an empire that encompassed America, Canada, Haiti and Venezuela.

Although moral outrage played some part in Darby's decision, there was self-interest too. These two vice lords had begun to look upon the clubs of Soho and the West End as happy hunting grounds for the prostitutes under their control. And it was often difficult for a club-owner to differentiate between a paid professional and an amorous lady in search of romance.

Darby was currently on good terms with the police, who were prepared to look the other way when a bit of gang warfare was involved and even to tolerate a certain degree of protection racketeering. But he knew attitudes would change if it became suspected that the clubs controlled by the Sabinis were allowing vice to flourish.

With such lawless men as Allard and Vernon, the feud inevitably ended in bloodshed. In fact, it ended on January 24th, 1936, with the discovery of a bullet-ridden corpse with manicured hands, a scarred face and patent leather shoes in a ditch outside St Albans. Red Max's reign was over.

Nutty Sharpe was put in charge of the murder investigation and soon found that the killing had taken place in the Little Newport Street flat of Vernon's mistress, Suzanne Naylor (alias Suzanne Bertron). The body had been transported to St Albans by car.

By then Vernon and his mistress had fled to Paris, where they were arrested and tried before a French court. Vernon was found guilty of the murder, but escaped the guillotine and was returned to Devil's Island after being sentenced to ten years' penal servitude and banished from France for twenty years. Suzanne Naylor was acquitted of complicity.

During the trial, it had been said that Red Max owed Vernon twenty-five pounds and that refusal to pay this had acted as the final flashpoint in their feud.

One night in the Griffin, Alf White commented upon this, shaking his head sorrowfully and saying, "Just think, twenty-five pounds for the death of a man!"

Darby was unmoved. "This wasn't a man," he said. "This was a monster."

21

THE LAST HURRAH

*"I suggest that you are the king of the Sabini
Gang" — Charge made by counsel in the
Bankruptcy Court. Darby's reply : "You must
surely be mistaking me for someone else. I'm
just a humble, peace-loving man."*

Darby sat on the balcony of his hotel's penthouse suite
overlooking the beach, its white sand running down to the
water. The sky was the kind of blue you normally only see
in picture postcards, and the faintest of summer breezes
ruffled his hair. He closed his eyes and turned his face to the
sun. It was a perfect day, marred by just the one flaw. Big
Alf White was coming to see him, trailing trouble in his
wake.

Viewed thus in what he regarded as his Brighton holiday
home, he made a remarkable contrast to the Darby of
Clerkenwell. The Grand Hotel, the ultimate in South
Coast luxury, seemed a million miles away from the hovel
on Saffron Hill that he still called home. Instead of the
grime of London Town, the brilliant white front of the hotel
shimmered in the morning sunshine. Instead of the city
smoke, there were sea breezes and cool, clean air.

And like a chameleon, Darby himself had changed. The
eternal cap, the muffler, the collarless shirt and the dark
rough suit had been discarded. In their place he wore tennis
shoes, white slacks and a blue open-neck shirt. He had the
look of a man who had been surrounded by the fine things
of life for all his days.

At the Grand he was known as Charles Sullivan, the
name he had once fought under, having borrowed the

surname from his manager and occasional employer Dan Sullivan. There was nothing sinister in this. It was just that he had acquired a taste for respectability. He had always looked upon himself as an honest man. Now he very much wanted the world at large to regard him that way too. He wondered whether he'd ever be able to walk into a restaurant without someone nudging their neighbour and pointing him out as a gangster chief.

He was still wondering about this when Alf White arrived, looking gravely astonished at the luxury wrapped around his long-time commander.

Darby took a bottle of wine from the ice bucket and filled their glasses. "Here's to the good old days," he said, raising his glass in salute.

"We'll never know a better day," said White, and then shading his eyes, this lover of quotations stared across the bay to the distant cliffs and added, 'a land fit for heroes' — a reference to David Lloyd George's well-meant promise to troops in the Kaiser's War.

Darby smiled slightly. "Now, old friend," he said, "you haven't come all this way just simply to drink my wine and talk about the view. So tell me what you've really come to say."

For the first time White appeared ill at ease, but he didn't hesitate. "My sons want to go their own way, to break away from the Sabinis."

Darby, who had been expecting, this showed no emotion. "That's what your sons want, Alf. Now tell me what *you* want. That's what I'd like to hear."

The big man sighed and said, "I reckon they're right, Darby. I reckon this is the time to go."

White had been with Darby from the very beginning, and in all that time there had never been an angry word between them. So Darby, more puzzled than hurt, asked, "Alf, have I ever treated you badly, ever treated you in any other fashion than that of a friend?"

White shook his head. "No, you've always been fair."

Darby continued as though his counsellor hadn't spoken. "You're a good fighting-man, hand-to-hand on the cobbles; but like Georgie and me you don't like the cutting, so I never sent you out with the teams. I always looked after you in my way, made sure you received the respect you deserved. Now I can understand your boys wanting to do their own thing. The young are always ambitious, but I don't understand you. Why this sudden change?"

White shrugged, and for the first time there was a trace of bitterness. "It's not me who's changed," he said. "It's you. There was a time when Little Italy marked the boundaries of your ambitions. Now you're spending more and more days down here living like a millionaire. You used to be a man who only wanted to protect his people. Now you're the head of a business empire. Twenty years ago, I was living in Covent Garden, and I'm still living there today. That's why the boys want to break away. It's time for them to move up in the world too."

This was something Darby understood; and then suddenly he understood Big Alf's reasons too. At the start he had been very much Darby's right-hand man. Darby rarely planned any move without first consulting his counsellor. Then Georgie Sewell had arrived to become Darby's closest companion, and so usurped the position that White had regarded as his own.

And now new messiahs were rising in Little Italy, men much younger than Big Alf and more Mediterranean in their ways. Nino Zoff still had his band of followers who could put fear into the hearts of any other gang in the land. Angelo Gardini, with his mixture of charm and ruthlessness, was seemingly Darby's heir-apparent. And now there was an even younger contender named Alberto Dimeo, who would become better known as Albert Dimes.

He had been born in Saffron Hill and taken under the wing of Bert Marsh, but it was Darby's star that he wished to follow. He was a sturdy young man, quietly spoken and yet never known to take a backward step. Already some of the older Italians were hailing him as the new Darby. So for White, the prospect of any future high command with the

Sabinis must have seemed remote.

Blaming himself a little, Darby decided to make one last peace move.

"We've been friends a long time," he said. "If there is something more that you want, a bigger slice of the cake, all you have to do is ask. You know I'm a reasonable man. But if you still wish to break away, there is nothing I can do to stop you. However, think on this. At the moment you have your own regime under the protection of the Sabini family; but if you go, the protection goes too. You would be out there alone in a dog-eat-dog world. And who knows, if our interests clash we could even come to a day when we would be enemies rather than friends. For me, that would be a sad day."

Big Alf rose. "It will never happen," he said, "you have my hand on it." And so saying he reached out and clasped Darby's hand in both of his. But for such a normally forthright man, his words lacked conviction and he failed to meet Darby's eye. And in that moment Darby finally sensed the truth. The Whites weren't merely breaking away from the Sabinis. They were about to make a bid for gangland supremacy.

Darby stayed on the balcony for a while. The sky was still an impossible blue. The sunlight still shimmered across the water; but for Darby the magic had gone. A good day had turned into a very bad one.

As time rolled by, Lady Diana's relationship with Angelo had changed. They had become friends rather than lovers. They still made wild love when the need was upon them; but it was now more a way of chasing away the blues than a grand passion.

Angelo had told her that one day he would marry Sandra Mancini, and that confession had given her no pain. It even amused her a little that Angelo, with his old-fashioned Sicilian ways, would sleep with her, but not with his bride-to-be. He said he wanted to marry a virgin, although of course everyone knew that Sandra's virginity had been lost on the long road to Birmingham.

But now all of a sudden their pleasant relationship had been threatened by a phone call from Angelo's gold-toothed commander. Darby had summoned Angelo to Brighton. He hadn't explained the reason or said how long he wished him to stay. Yet Angelo, without a moment's hesitation, was already packing his bag.

"Darby needs me," he told Lady Diana.

She sighed. "Doesn't it occur to you, Angelo, that I might need you too?"

There was a note of entreaty in her voice which, in his haste to finish packing, he misunderstood. "No one's going to trouble you while I'm away," he said. "The name of Sabini is for you a magic shield. And anyway, if you have even a whisper of discontent call Nino and he'll come running. Believe me, no club in London is better protected."

If he'd looked at her that moment he might have recognised the desperation in her eyes.

"Do you really have to go to him like some small boy every time he calls?" she asked.

Angelo smiled slightly. "Darby is not the kind of man who shies at shadows. When he calls there is always a reason. Men have tried to kill him before and maybe one day they'll succeed; but not when I'm around."

"But why does it always have to be you?" she asked. "He has so many men."

Angelo's smile became broader. "Because I'm a very special man." He paused. "I thought you knew that."

He didn't like to admit the real reason even to himself. With the possible exception of Alfie Solomons, he was the only murderer within the ranks of the Sabinis, certainly the only assassin, the only one prepared to go all the way ... and this reputation made him an object of very special terror to Darby's enemies.

When the cab drew up outside the Charmaine, she said quietly, "I hate goodbyes, so just kiss me, my darling, and hurry home."

But as they kissed she found herself clinging to him in sudden fear. She watched him walk away and give one last wave; and she was filled with a terrible premonition that she had just kissed him goodbye for ever.

Following the departure of the Whites, Darby would normally have used the Jewish wing of the organisation, commanded by Alfie Solomons and known as the Yiddisher Mob, to shore up his defences. But for years this had been little more than a marriage of convenience. They had stayed together simply because their interests coincided. The Yiddishers were mostly members of the bookmakers' fraternity. The Sabinis were the supreme power on the racecourses of Southern England, and so it was a neat businesslike relationship, but that was all. Following the fatal stabbing of Buck Emden, Darby had probably saved Solomons from the hangman; but by so doing he seemingly hadn't bought his loyalty. And now that he needed them most, the Yiddishers decided to desert Darby too.

He still had the hard core of his army; but suddenly there were chinks in his armour, and rival gangs who hadn't dared to oppose him for over a decade began plotting to avenge past wrongs.

The Hoxton Mob, neighbours and traditional enemies of the Sabinis, decided that this was the moment to resume the racecourse wars. They chose Lewes as their battleground; and within the hour Darby, the great spymaster, knew about their plans. He used the same tactics that he had used on a distant day in Brighton. He told his followers to stay away from the course and tipped off the police.

So on the appointed day, the Flying Squad were lying in wait. They spotted some thirty members of the Hoxton Mob walking beside the bookmakers' stands and clearly looking for the Sabinis.

One of them was heard to say, "It's no good here, boys, there are too many top-hats [detectives]."

Then another shouted, "Here they are, boys, get your tools ready," and they started running towards Alfie

Solomons and his clerk, Mark Frater. As they ran, they produced weapons from under their coats, hatchets, knuckle-dusters, hammers and bars of iron.

Solomons received several blows on the head, but managed to escape. Frater wasn't so fortunate. One man held his arm, while another struck him on the head with a hatchet. In all probability the arrival of the police saved his life. The mob scattered their weapons on the grass and attempted to flee. Some were grabbed instantly. Others were caught in a car as they attempted to make a getaway.

One of them was discovered lying on his back in some bushes, attempting to hide. "All right, mate, I'm only resting," he told a police officer.

"In that case," said the officer, arresting him, "come and rest with me."

Sixteen of the mob subsequently faced trial at Lewes Assizes. Mr Justice Hilbery suggested to Frater that he shouldn't look at the men in the dock while telling his story to the jury; but even so he was unable to identify his assailants.

"I submit to you," said prosecuting counsel John Flowers, "that he was absolutely terrified of giving evidence of identification against any one of these men."

Friends of the accused raised one thousand pounds for their defence, but all to no avail. After three hours' deliberation, the jury found them all guilty.

The judge told them: "By the mercy of Providence, Frater wasn't killed. I say by the mercy of Providence ... I perhaps ought to add also, through the alertness of the police and the prompt execution by the police of their duty. It certainly was not through any mercy that any of you were disposed to show your victim.

"You had armed yourselves with weapons which have been aptly described as villainous instruments to use upon any fellow human being.

"You showed no mercy to your victim, and you intended to show no mercy. Crimes of gang violence in this country will meet with no mercy.

"Gang violence is not only a brutal breach of our law, but it also exercises terror on its victims. You men hoped to escape, and I have not the least doubt that in this case you thought that because Frater would not dare, for fear of you, to identify one of you, that you might escape.

"There is no case here for leniency. You will receive sentences which I hope will teach you once and for all that crimes of this sort do not pay in this country, and which will teach others who are listening here or who may read what happened in this case afterwards."

His Lordship then sentenced the sixteen men to a grand total of forty-three and a half years' imprisonment.

As for the racecourse wars, this was to prove 'The Last Hurrah'. Following this June fracas in 1936, a relative calm descended over the racetracks.

Once again, Darby by his foresight had kept his ranks unscathed; and there had to be a certain irony in the fact that Solomons, the renegade Sabini, had been the only Sabini to suffer.

But Darby's wisdom wasn't absolute. When a Sunday newspaper wrote a series of articles about the race gangs, he rashly sued ... and even more rashly failed to appear at the hearing in the High Courts. So judgment was given against him in default and he was ordered to pay the costs of £775.

He then filed a petition for bankruptcy, producing a statement that showed debts of just over £800 and assets nil.

He was once more attired in his humble peasant's uniform and stood there holding his cap in his hand.

He looked gravely surprised when the counsel for the creditors said, "I suggest that you are the king of the Sabini Gang."

"You must surely be mistaking me for someone else," replied Darby. "I'm just a humble, peace-loving man."

Counsel pressed on, "And that you make between £20,000 and £30,000 a year."

At this, Darby threw up his hands in total bewilderment. "Now I know you have me confused with someone else," he said.

Afterwards he walked down Carey Street and turned left up Chancery Lane, where the Cobblestone Fighter was waiting in the powder-blue Buick.

"Would you like a drink?" asked Georgie.

Darby settled back into the seat and stretched out his legs. "Do you reckon I could afford one?" he replied.

22

END OF AN EMPIRE

"We have fought our wars, you and I, and won them long ago. I'm finished, old friend, with that sort of life" — Darby Sabini announcing his retirement from gangland to Georgie Sewell.

The first cracks in the foundations of the Sabini empire were not created by any artifice on the part of the forces of law and order. They came about by civil decree. The hovels of Little Italy were declared unfit for human habitation and thereby razed to the ground. And so in one fell swoop the power base of Darby Sabini had been destroyed. The impregnable fortress had gone. So too had the barrack rooms and the recruiting grounds.

But for their gold-toothed commander, the effects went even deeper. He no longer had a reason for continuing the battle. He had always prided himself upon being the Godfather of Little Italy, the lord high protector of his people. In his view it lifted him above the other gang leaders. It was almost by holy writ.

Now, with his people scattered all over the city and beyond his help, the crusade was over. From a more practical point of view, many of his most lucrative ventures became impossible to maintain simply because there was no physical presence to back them up.

How, for instance, could you carry out raids on rival territories when there was no safe base to return to in the early hours of the morning? How could you control the clubs when your soldiers couldn't be summoned at the first hint of trouble? Even the barbershop of Jimmy Sabatini, the

Clutching Hand, had gone, and with it the means of ready communication with the mob.

So like the accomplished commander that he was, he ordered a tactical withdrawal. He moved out of clubland. He disbanded his part-time soldiers, retained only his hard-core mobsters and became simply a racecourse gangster. Brighton, a town by the sea that he had long enjoyed, became his new home and a base too for many of his followers. The repercussions of that move were felt throughout the underworld and beyond. He had for so long been the ultimate power, the commander to be feared above all others; and now almost casually, so it seemed, he had abdicated that authority. Much of his kingdom was up for grabs. So too was the position of gangland supremacy.

Fresh wars broke out between the rival mobs who had suddenly glimpsed gold. New messiahs emerged with dreams of becoming the next Sabini. And many club-owners who had groaned beneath the yoke found themselves with good reason to mourn his departure. With that odd sense of fearful righteousness that had been his hallmark, he had always insisted upon keeping his word.

You might pay heavily for being under the protection of the Sabinis; but it was never a token shield, never a case of money demanded without any sign of service in return. Your interests would be guarded by the gun, the knife, the razor and the knuckleduster. If you had troubles, you needed only to talk to Darby and your troubles became his. Naturally, there was a price to be paid for such services. He was after all a businessman, but that price was never totally unreasonable, never crippling. That too was good business. What could be gained by forcing your customers to close their doors?

But in the wake of the Sabinis there came a band of men, crueller, more mercenary, less far-sighted than the ones who had gone before. They took their money at gun-point, and club-owners who attempted to debate the point were beaten up, their establishments wrecked. Nor was anything given in return other than the devious promise that they would no longer be molested by their protectors. True, these new overlords of clubland would fight off rival mobsters, but only in the manner of dogs who will guard their bones from other hungry curs.

Otherwise they evinced no interest in the smooth running of such establishments. The run-of-the-mill trouble-makers were allowed to go unchecked. The bar-room bullies were no longer given a sharp lesson in manners by the likes of a Georgie Sewell or a Massarda. Gangland had reached a pretty pass.

The Cerdan Brothers were specialists in the delicate art of waxing rich upon the labours of their womenfolk. Pimps were no strangers to London Town. They had been around since the days of Good King Charles; but the Cerdan Brothers had brought a new dimension to the business. They controlled entire regiments of girls upon the streets, around the night clubs and in luxury apartments. They catered for every sexual appetite known to mankind. Some of these were so way-out, so extreme, that the girls demurred. But not for long. The Brothers ruled their girls with a firm hand, and would find it necessary from time to time to teach lessons in obedience.

This posed no problem to these men from Bruges; for in addition to all their other talents, they were masters in the art of torture. And no girl who'd ever suffered at their hands had been known to err again. Such lessons became for the Cerdans much more than a business expedient. They became a labour of love.

The four brothers, Carlo, Michael, Henri and Max, always insisted upon giving such lessons personally. It was a mark of their genius that they also contrived to make a profit from such adventures. There was a small band of very rich men, followers of the Marquis de Sade, who were prepared to pay very heavily indeed for the opportunity to view these very private teachings. And of course in the days that followed an account of these happenings would spread like wildfire amongst the girls in the employ of the Brothers;

and that too served its purpose. Thereafter they proved even more anxious to please, to satisfy the wildest whims. It was a neat arrangement.

Such was the terror that the Brothers inspired that only one woman, Lady Diana of the Charmaine, had ever dared to stand up against them. Sensing the rich pickings which could be harvested from the youthful aristocrats in that exclusive clientele, they had forcibly recruited some of the club's hostesses.

The girls had been far too scared either to resist or complain, but Lady Diana had called in the police ... her friend the Commissioner, no less. Despite dire warnings delivered by the Brothers in person, she had given evidence in court; and as a result of her intervention, two of the Cerdan hirelings had gone to jail. It was something that as businessmen the Brothers couldn't ignore. Otherwise the courts could soon be filled with complainants. They decided to hand out the same lesson to Lady Diana that they had handed out to scores of other disobedient women ... only in her case, they promised themselves some rather special pleasures.

Lady Diana was bored. Sundays had always been the days she hated most of all. Sundays were lonely days. On all the other days of the week, she could remind herself that the doors of the Charmaine would open and that there would at least be people around her; but on Sundays, by city ordinance, they stayed closed. Now, as it was still the early part of the afternoon, she wondered seriously how she could possibly survive the empty hours that stretched out in front of her.

Ever since Angelo had been recalled by Darby to act as his lieutenant in Brighton, she had been toying with the idea of selling the Charmaine and moving on to some fresh adventure where she might at least find peace of mind. But although she barely admitted it to herself, she had lingered on in the faint hope that Angelo might one day return. Six months after his going she still missed him terribly, grieved for him more fiercely than any lover in any romance. And her dreams were not the dreams of a young girl, or those of a longing wife. She was not rendered desolate by the loss of her life companion. Nor did she pretend to herself that she had been in love with him. No, she missed him for the more important reason that he had been the only man in the world who could make her happy, chase away the loneliness.

Because she had tutored him in the arts of love, he had become for her the most perfect bedmate. His youth, his romantic Latin ways, could make her laugh; and seemingly none of the smooth playboys who peopled her life nowadays could do that any more.

She was still thinking of Angelo when the doorbell chimed down on the street below. She took a quick glance out of the window to discover who her caller might be, but he was hidden from view by the canopy. Even so, she didn't really care who it might be on such a day. Any caller would be welcome. She hurried down the stairs and was dismayed when she could see no silhouette through the glass panels of the door. Had he already gone away?

She threw open the door, and instantly Carlo Cerdan — who had been standing to one side — stepped over the threshold. Too late she tried to close the door. He pushed his way in, followed by his three brothers. Their method was brutally efficient. Carlo placed a rough hand over her mouth and seized an arm. Michael took the other arm. Henri and Max grabbed a leg apiece and they proceeded to carry her struggling, feet-first, up the stairs to her apartment.

So far not a single word had been spoken. Once back in her room, Carlo sat beside her on the plush velvet divan, keeping that hand still clamped across her mouth, that cruel grip still upon her arm, and sent his brothers out to search the premises. They returned shortly to announce that the Charmaine was totally deserted, and at this unholy joy showed in the eyes of Carlo.

He took his hand away. "Just you and us," he said, "and

a long afternoon and evening in front of us. Now what could be nicer than that?"

Lady Diana, still recovering from the struggle, was breathing fast. "What do you want of me?" she asked, and was ashamed at the quiver in her voice.

Carlo smiled cruelly. "You've caused us a lot of trouble," he said. "The boys and I just thought we'd call round and hear you say you were sorry." He chuckled at his own humour.

"Oh, I'm sorry all right," said Lady Diana, regaining her spirit. "Sorry that you weren't the ones to go to jail. And don't imagine for a moment that the Commissioner won't hear of this visit."

She was still more angry than frightened, and this reaction delighted the Brothers. The majority of the girls they disciplined were reduced at an early stage to tearful pleas. They already sensed that Lady Diana, this blue-blooded and very beautiful aristocrat, would make a pleasant change. They would take their time taming that pride, and then later would come the abject fear.

Carlo spoke to her chidingly, as a teacher might speak to a child. "You have led a very sheltered life," he said, "far removed from the real world. But today it is time for you to rejoin the common herd, to learn the lessons that every other girl who crosses us has to learn. Namely, that there are moments when neither a title nor powerful friends can help you at all.

"In a little while we will take those fine clothes away from you, and then naked you will look like any other little shop-girl. You will feel the same kind of pain, cry the same stupid tears and plead very prettily for mercy. Only in your case, mercy may be slow in coming. You have displeased us, caused us public embarrassment, and therefore your punishment must be more severe than most. And when it's all over, I can promise you that you'll never again threaten us with this talk of Commissioners. Your only wish will be that you never anger us again."

He added almost jovially: "But let's have a drink together

first. On such a day we should enjoy only the very best champagne."

Michael, the youngest of the brothers, fetched two bottles of champagne. The curtains were drawn, the doors securely bolted, the windows shuttered to give every impression of an empty house. For the best part of an hour they waited, playing with her the way a cat plays with a mouse, mocking, taunting; letting the fear mount on her part, and the lust on theirs. And then finally when the playing ended, they stripped her with brutal roughness, tearing her clothes to shreds; simply because they had discovered on days gone by that girls have a sentimental attachment to such things.

She fought them desperately every step along the way, and this merely added to their pleasures. They were surprised as others had been surprised before them by the fullness and the perfection of her figure, and her nakedness delighted them.

They took turns in beating her with a swagger cane that had been carefully selected from their collection of instruments of pain. Despite herself Lady Diana was crying out with every stroke, so they gagged her with her own stockings and continued beating her until she was red and raw.

"Are you ready to plead for mercy now?" asked Carlo, removing the gag, and she swore at him, using a fine mixture of Anglo-Saxon words.

He slapped her face with sufficient force to rock her head violently, and by now all pretence at a rough-handed humour had long gone. The Brothers' faces reflected brutal joy. Any pleas for mercy would have been a total waste of time. Their pleasures were only just beginning, and her pride and spirit only added to them.

Replacing the gag even more tightly than before, they proceeded to brand her with the glowing tips of their cigars. They still behaved like men who were in no hurry at all to end the entertainment; and finally she fainted into merciful oblivion. But even that respite was short-lived. She recovered to discover them drinking another round of champagne, still viewing her with lustful, merciless eyes.

And then almost as an anticlimax they raped her. They took turns. The elder brother Carlo first followed in seniority by Michael, Henri and Max. They even removed the gag in the hope that they would hear her pleas for mercy, but instead she continued to curse them.

However, when it was all over she was wise enough not to utter any more threats. She believed that men as wild as these, men with such a low opinion of the female race, must hover forever on the brink of murder.

So they left her there in her nakedness with her burns, her bruises and her degradation. She put on a robe and for several hours she remained staring out at the slowly darkening city. Then with the inborn tidiness of the female, she collected her torn clothes and put them away in a cupboard.

She wrote a note for Angelo. And eventually she went to bed with two full bottles of brandy and enough pain-killers to destroy six strong men; and in the morning they found her dead.

She hadn't killed herself through any true sense of shame. She hadn't felt the need for any. Nor was she old-fashioned enough to believe herself ruined for ever.

No, she killed herself for what she considered the best of all reasons. She was lonely and without hope.

Darby was dressed in his gardening uniform: corduroy trousers, open-necked faded blue shirt and the inevitable cap upon his head. Only this cap was sober grey, unlike the check one he'd flaunted in the days of kingship. He told everyone that he worked in his garden for the sake of his health; but he deceived no one. The truth was that he loved tending his garden. He loved the sight of the flowers as they opened their petals to the first sunlight of the day; and most of all he loved the scent of the roses.

Today he sat in a deckchair on the lawn of his Brighton home talking to Georgie Sewell; and for the moment the talk was of flowers. Like most violent men who have discovered a peaceful pleasure, Darby had been surprised to find that this pleasure was shared by an even more violent man. Yet the Cobblestone Fighter's interest was no casual one. With the aid of Hetty, he had run a florist's business for the past ten years and become a considerable authority on the countless varieties which could bloom in an English garden.

When Darby had first moved to the South Coast the salt breezes had ruined the flowers he'd purchased so hopefully, burnt the tender leaves, blown away the early blossoms.

So he had consulted his warlord and stocked his garden with hardier annuals, built his fences higher to keep the wind at bay and dug out a sunken rose bower.

But he knew, of course, that the Cobblestone Fighter hadn't come all this way just to talk about the flowers. He was a man never really happy away from the streets of London. Some people dream of sultry summer afternoons beside the sea, but he was never one of those. He would have preferred a London drizzle any day.

So finally Darby asked the question he'd been trying to put behind him. "Is it bad?" he asked.

"Bad enough," answered Georgie. "Epsom is up for grabs; and now that Solomons and Alf White have taken their teams away, we're not really in business. Even the small bookies are refusing to pay us their dues, and you can't blame them. We can't protect them."

Darby shrugged, the most casual of gestures. "So what advice do you give me?" he asked.

Sewell studied his man closely before answering and was seemingly discouraged by what he saw. "It's not like the old days," he said. "This new lot are a bunch of impostors. You and I backed by twelve good fighting men could chase them off the tracks in a day. We could put such fear in them that they'd never come back. They've had it too easy. They're amateurs at the game. One spanking from some real pro's is all they need to get them running."

Darby sighed. "I'm too old for that sort of game, Georgie; and you and I don't need it any more. That's something best left to the boys and to the young men. Once it made sense, because in Little Italy we had no choice. It was either fight or lay down, so we fought. But those days are long gone. No one threatens me or my people any more. I have good neighbours who treat me like an honest man. And I have everything I need, enough money to wash away the worries, three lovely daughters and a handsome son. What more could a man want?"

He paused. "You have a good wife and two fine sons, so you must surely understand what I'm saying. I don't really care any more what happens on the racecourses. That's all in the past. We have fought our wars, you and I, and won them long ago. I'm finished, old friend, with that sort of life."

The Cobblestone Fighter didn't say anything for a while, and when the words came they surprised Darby, who had been expecting an argument.

For all he said was, "All right, if you're finished, I'm finished too."

He could have explained that, without Darby, all the meaning and much of the fun would have gone out of the game; that he was maybe the nearest thing to a friend he'd ever known. But that was never his way.

So when he finally left with the twilight softening the land, he merely shook Darby's hand and held it a fraction longer than usual.

"I hope you find your peace," he said.

But for Darby, peace would be all too brief. On the night that Italy came into the war, angry mobs besieged Italian restaurants and clubs, often attacking men who had been their friends for years. Many of Darby's comrades and friends were arrested and interned on the Isle of Man, labelled as undesirable aliens. And some of his neighbours began to look the other way whenever he walked down the street.

Just three months later, Darby was jailed for the first time in his life on a receiving charge. And although there had been many sins for which he could have been justly imprisoned, this wasn't one of them. On this charge he was as innocent as a new-born babe; and it underlined more clearly than anything else the depth of his decline.

A few years earlier, he would have hired a team of lawyers that would have made nonsense of such a charge. Or failing that he would have bribed a few witnesses, pulled a few strings and had the charge wiped off the books. But now he was paying the price for having decided to become an honest man. He was suddenly that much more vulnerable than he had been before.

If he had been framed by the Birmingham Boys, the Hoxton Mob or the Elephant Gang, he could have accepted that with equanimity. They had after all been his enemies. But this time he knew that he had been betrayed by one of his former allies, either Alf White or Alfie Solomons, or more probably both working in unison; and he found this hard to understand. He had always been loyal to his friends, even to former friends.

He tried to stop Maria visiting him in Lewes Jail. It offended his pride to have her see him in his grey prison uniform, to talk to him through a wire mesh while a warder standing by could hear every word spoken. But she came just the same, sitting there dressed in black, still more Italian than the natives of that country.

She would tell him about his garden at home, about the children who never came, and about the war which was beginning to run the Allies' way.

And then one day, although she talked more volubly than ever, Darby sensed that something was wrong. He had noted today that the warders seemed kinder, that as soon as Maria was seated, there were quick secretive glances and they were left for once totally alone.

So he smiled a little at this wife of his whom he respected, but had never fully understood. "Don't you think you should tell me now what everyone else seems to know?"

To his consternation Maria began to sob. He waited her out and then he said, "Now tell me what is this thing you find so difficult to tell your husband." There was just the faintest hint of reproach for her weakness.

"Your son Johnny has been shot down in action," she said flatly. "He's dead." Now that the words had been said, she was no longer weeping.

Darby blinked. For just the fraction of a second, the wall of his will disintegrated and the draining of his physical strength was plain on his face. Then he recovered.

He clasped his hands in front of him on top of the shelf that lay between them and looked directly into Maria's eyes. "Is there no hope," he said, "no hope that he may have made it after all?"

"No hope at all," she said firmly, and it was as though she had borrowed some of his strength.

He accepted this final verdict without any sign of emotion except for a few moments of silence. Then he said, "So be it. Now all we have to do is shield his sisters from grief and bury our son as best we can."

But that was something Darby couldn't do. His request to attend his son's funeral was turned down by the prison governor; and it was this act of cold-hearted bureaucracy which finally broke the seemingly unbreakable man.

He lost all desire to live and very soon after leaving prison he died, some said of a broken heart.

His old comrades, Georgie Sewell, Angelo Gardini, Nino Zoff and Pasquala Poppa visited him on his deathbed. And he asked them to ensure that he be buried as befits an honest man, and not in some great gangland cavalcade.

That last wish was honoured. He was given a quiet funeral, just family and a few close friends. Silvio Massarda was there, all enmity long forgotten, and so too was Jack Capstick standing shoulder to shoulder with the Cobblestone Fighter. As the final prayers were being read, the Scotland Yard commander removed a red rose from his buttonhole and placed it on the coffin of his old friend.

So this simple peasant who became a king was laid quietly to rest.

23

THE LONG GOODBYE

*"Tell me, my husband, why should a man carry
a gun on his wedding day?" — Sandra's question
for Angelo Gardini.*

It was a wedding in the old Italian style. A mandolin band played Mediterranean melodies. Guests danced on wooden platforms while others sat at tables loaded with Neapolitan delicacies and jugs of home-made wine. The bride, Sandra Mancini, sat in splendour at a specially raised table with her groom Angelo beside her. She thought him incredibly handsome, and was in a fever of impatience for the honeymoon to begin.

They were to have been married a week earlier, but Darby's death had changed that. Angelo had insisted upon observing a proper spell of mourning, and this past week had been the longest she could remember. But Angelo still appeared to have all the time in the world. He kissed her lightly on the cheek, and rose. "Let's mingle with our guests," he said. "Who knows, some we may never see again."

That prophecy seemed likely to come all too true. Tonight they would sail on a luxury liner to America to begin a new life in Brooklyn under the protection of Joseph Profaci, one of New York's most powerful Mafia bosses. Angelo had family links with his fellow-Sicilian.

Their luggage was already on the boat, and as Angelo drifted around the room chatting to old friends, he frequently glanced at his watch. After all, luxury liners wait for no one, not even for newly-weds. Their eventual departure was a hurried one, spurred on by lewd and good-natured taunts from the older Italians about the impatience of young lovers. And then they were clambering into the back of Silvio Massarda's Bugatti, waving, blowing kisses, crying out fond farewells which were all terminated when Massarda engaged the clutch and set off on scorching tyres.

Sandra happily brushed the rice out of her hair and smoothed down the pale-blue dress of watered silk which Darby had given her many moons ago. She caught Massarda watching her warmly in the rear-view mirror and winked knowingly at him. She had always liked Massarda, and listened with avid interest to all the tales told about him by the other Italian girls. The scars on his face were now little more than a thin white line against the deep tan; and to her eyes they gave him a buccaneering look, making him even more dashing than before.

At one time, she had secretly hoped he might make a pass at her; but that was of course before Angelo had entered her life. She had never allowed herself to forget how much she owed him; and now engulfed with tenderness, she slid her arms around him.

Oblivious to the presence of Massarda, she started to caress Angelo, and then suddenly she stopped. Her hand had come to rest on a gun tucked into the waistband of his trousers.

She drew back, more puzzled than alarmed. "Tell me, my husband," she said, "why should a man carry a gun on his wedding day?"

Out of the corner of her eye she saw Massarda stiffen, but still joking she asked, "Could it be that you feel the need to defend yourself against the amorous demands of your wife?"

However, as soon as she glanced at Angelo's face she knew there would be no answering jest. She had never seen him more serious. He took her chin between thumb and forefinger so that her eyes met his, and then speaking very slowly and very clearly he said: "I have only time to say this once. So listen very closely. There can be no arguments. I have one last thing to do before I leave, something that as a man of honour I can't leave undone. So whatever happens you must stay in the car with Silvio. If I don't return within twenty minutes, Silvio will drive on and you must go with him. You must forget you ever saw the gun. Silvio will take my place on the boat and see you arrive safely in Brooklyn. He already has the tickets; and if I'm still all right, I'll join you later."

He had barely finished speaking when the Bugatti drew up at the pavement edge. He kissed her briefly, broke away from her clutching hands and slipped out of the car, followed by her wail of despair. But Italian traditions die hard. She remained inside the car as commanded, although every instinct warned her that she was about to become a widow on her wedding day.

Georgie Sewell had also observed seven days of mourning for Darby. And now he was about to pay his last debt to the man whom he'd admired above all others. He was dressed as though it was his own wedding day, spotless white shirt, shoes shining, suit brushed, diamond stick-pin in his tie and the faithful curly-brimmed bowler square upon his head.

But unlike Angelo he wasn't heading for the church. He was heading for the White Hart in St. Martin's Lane, which had become the gangland haunt of Alfie Solomons and the other Sabinis who had deserted Darby for richer pastures. It was an act he could neither forgive nor understand. In his eyes the issue was crystal clear. Darby had saved Solomons from the hangman's noose, and therefore he owed Darby his life.

Solomons should have been prepared to serve him to his dying day. To have turned against Darby in his hour of need was treachery of the basest kind; and the account was long overdue for settling.

Alfie Solomons was sitting comfortably in his favourite chair in the White Hart, and was surveying the bar-room with a satisfied eye. He just had to look around him to feel the delicious tug of power. Seventeen of his ruffians were propping up the bar. The other customers stepped quietly around him. He only had to frown at a man to see the flicker of fear.

The killing of Buck Emden had changed his world, transformed him from a small-time hoodlum into a gang leader in his own right, a dangerous man with a deadly reputation. He studied the girls behind the bar, knowing he could take his choice. That too was one of the rewards that came with the big time. He was wondering which one it would be when he caught sight of Georgie Sewell coming through the swing doors.

The initial sense of shock was followed by one of fierce, pagan pleasure. There had always been bad blood between them. He remembered how in his early Sabini days this Cobblestone Fighter had always been the one anxious to cut him down to size.

He remembered the night in the Fratalanza when Sewell, contemptuous of the gun in his hand, had knocked him cold. And he remembered how at the party to celebrate his return from jail, Sewell had pushed through the ranks of the young Italian admirers and said, "At least Buck was a man ..."

He had never hated a man with such venom as he hated this one, and now at long last a kind fate had delivered this enemy into his hands. He was surprised that Sewell, normally so wise in the ways of violence, should have made such a tactical mistake. Even in his prime the Cobblestone Fighter wouldn't have dared buck such odds. Now with his days behind him, he didn't have even the glimmer of a chance. Solomons had merely to give the signal and his seventeen henchmen would cut Sewell to ribbons. Determined to make sure that his prey shouldn't escape him now, Solomons gave a quick nod to a hoodlum standing by the doors and the bolts were slid home, thus isolating the bar from the street outside.

Sewell heard the bolts slam, saw Solomons' henchmen lining the bar, but none of this showed on his face. He was smiling, seemingly without a care in the world, pleased to meet former comrades in arms. They watched him come towards them, gleeful anticipation tinged with caution. Even now, despite the overwhelming odds, the aura of fear still lingered on. They waited a little longer, curious as to what he'd do or say; and when he did speak, he surprised them all.

The memory of Darby and a distant day at Brighton came back to him and he called out, "Drinks for all my friends," and the girls behind the bar who had become frozen by the unmistakable scent of violence were suddenly galvanised back into action.

The drinks were placed upon the bar and Sewell raising his glass said, "To Darby, may God rest his soul." They drank to that with the odd sentimentality that is an essential facet of the gangster world.

Only the glass of Alfie Solomons remained untouched. He had decided that the moment for vengeance had come. Very distinctly he called out, "I'm not drinking with you, you bastard," and picking up the glass he went to throw its contents into the face of the Cobblestone Fighter.

But the lightning reflexes which had served Sewell so well down the years didn't fail him now. He ducked, and in the same movement hooked his man savagely to the head. What followed was so fast that men who had been standing just a few feet away were afterwards unable to describe what had happened. The sheer force and fury of Sewell's punching had seemingly pinned his man to the bar.

Although unconscious, he was unable to fall, and still those terrible hands came pounding down on their target. In the end it was a neutral, ex-boxer George Mills, who quelled some of the wildness in that wild man by shouting out, "For the love of God stop, Georgie, you've killed him."

And for the moment it did indeed look as though Solomons was a dead man. His face was so masked in blood, so featureless, that it didn't appear to be a face at all. But as he slipped down to the bar-room floor, a soft moan escaped from his mashed lips.

The screams of women had attracted the attention of passers-by. A crowd had gathered on the pavement, and two policemen were hammering on the door. By an odd irony, Solomons' forethought had saved his enemy from immediate arrest.

Sewell slipped behind the bar, found his way through to the tradesman's door, and with George Mills beside him stepped out into the street. His face was unmarked. He straightened his bowler, still a dapper man, thrust his mangled hands deep into his pockets and strolled casually past the growing crowd, whistling through his teeth.

Life had been good to the Cerdan Brothers. They had laboured and prospered. They now controlled the former West End empire of the Sabinis. They controlled the girls on the streets. They controlled the clubs. And they controlled many of the casinos too. The death of Lady Diana had proved to be no more than a passing embarrassment.

The Commissioner had asked a lot of questions; but as always the Brothers had an iron-clad alibi. As the undoubted cause of death was an overdose, even the Commissioner couldn't pursue enquiries indefinitely.

When the Charmaine was put up for sale, the Brothers bought it at about half its true market value, simply because there were no other bids. The reputation of these new crime czars had seen to that. The Charmaine had become their power base, giving them a surface respectability. They had converted Lady Diana's apartment into their private office, and it didn't spook them one whit to recall that this had been the setting for her last day on earth; and that they had been the ones who gave her that push into eternity.

On the contrary, the memory of that day gave them nothing but pleasure. It had widened their ambitions, given a new dimension to their games. They were no longer content simply to discipline the girls of the street who stepped out of line. They now concentrated on blue-blooded beauties, proud hoydens who reminded them of that long afternoon in the Charmaine.

Tonight they had promised themselves a very special treat. An eighteen-year-old named Arabella, the daughter of a duke, had walked into their carefully laid trap. They had encouraged her to gamble at their tables with limitless credit. They had whetted her appetite by letting her win for three nights in a row, sympathised with the losing streak that followed and then all of a sudden lowered the boom.

It was a case of £5,000 now or else; and just to make sure that she didn't ask her aristocratic dad to bail her out, they had dug the trap deeper still. One night, flushed with wine, she had been bedded by a gigolo, part of a small select band which the Brothers sprinkled around the clubs with blackmail in mind. And while she had been making love, the Brothers had gone to work with their cameras through a two-sided mirror.

Now in the manner of a gambler laying out a winning hand, Carlo had placed the pictures and the IOUs on the far side of the desk for the inspection of Arabella. She was so shaken that the words just wouldn't come. Yet even in that state of shock she was so lush, so lovely that the heart turned over just to look at her.

"You have been a very foolish girl," said Carlo, sounding more like a disappointed uncle than a cold-blooded lecher.

She nodded dumbly, and when it became clear that she was still incapable of speech, Carlo continued. "Of course as a responsible citizen," he said, "I should by rights send all these things to your father, so that he too can be made aware of your foolishness. That is my duty." He paused. "But I imagine you wouldn't wish me to do that."

"No, no, anything but that!" she cried, finding words at last. She had no doubts about the effects those pictures would have upon her father. If they didn't cause an instant coronary, by no means a remote possibility, they would put an end to their relationship. She would never be his daughter again. Love would die, and even worse, she would be cut off without the proverbial penny.

Carlo looked at his three brothers, Michael, Henri and Max, who all appeared solemn and stern as they played out this little comedy. And then as if acting against his better judgment, he said to them, "We have all been young in our time and know that to be foolish is often no more than a teenage malady. I'm a sentimental man at heart, and as such I have no wish to ruin the life of Arabella or cause undue pain to her innocent father. So do me this one favour. Let me settle the matter in my own way."

Slowly, with a show of reluctance, the Brothers gave their assent. But a more astute person than Arabella would have spotted the unholy joy building in their eyes.

Carlo turned back to her. "You see," he said, "we have decided to be kind. I will treat you as though you were my own daughter, and punish you in the same way that I would punish her if she disobeyed me. But when that has been done, the pictures and the IOUs will be yours to do with as you wish. There will be no recriminations, no ill feelings. The affair will never be mentioned again. Now, are you prepared to accept my punishment?"

Arabella nodded quickly, still with no notion of what that punishment might be, but fearful just the same. The Brothers let that fear build up by simply taking their time. They removed their jackets and placed them carefully across the backs of chairs. They rolled up their sleeves and loosened their neckties. And then still without a word of explanation or the slightest sign of hurry, they pulled the shutters across the windows. Since taking over the Charmaine, they had turned this room into a fortress.

The walls had been made six inches thicker than before. The door was solid oak banded by steel, and so heavy that six strong men had been required to place it in position. To put the final seal upon their privacy the Brothers had soundproofed the room, a sensible precaution on days such as this. After all, they didn't wish to have their guests on the floor below disturbed by the cries and the screams of Arabella. They now locked the door and were at long last ready to play their game.

It was at this moment that the bell rang. Due to the soundproofing, it was the only way contact could be made with those within. When there was no response, the caller put his thumb on the bell-push and kept it there. The minions of the Brothers were usually a little wiser than this.

With a muffled curse Carlo turned the key and opened the door, anxious to vent his anger. But instead his back stiffened and saying not a word he stepped back hastily. Angelo followed him into the room. There was a gun in Angelo's hand centred upon the spot directly between the eyes of Carlo.

The hand was steady and so was the voice. "Back up nice and steady," said Angelo, "one false move and you're a dead man." He spoke to the others. "Join your brother against the wall. And remember if anyone does something stupid, Carlo dies."

They obeyed, not because they were scared, but more because they were puzzled. Even in their early days, no one had ever been foolish enough to wave guns at the Brothers. Now that they were at the height of their power, surely only an innocent who didn't know their reputation or a madman would confront them in such a fashion. But as they were all too well aware, Angelo didn't fit into either category.

After the death of Lady Diana they had wondered about Angelo, wondered whether he would take it personally. It was beyond their understanding that a cool professional such as Angelo could ever consider going to war over a woman. As the weeks and the months had gone by without any sign of his displeasure, they had pushed the notion from their minds. Even now they couldn't bring themselves to believe that he had returned to avenge that ancient wrong.

As if to underline that opinion Angelo said, "Max, open up the safe," and the Brothers were puzzled no longer. Larceny was something they understood.

Angelo addressed Arabella without for a moment taking his eyes away from Carlo. "Lady, move away from the others. Sit down against the far wall. Do as you're told and no harm will come to you."

Ever since he'd first stepped into the room, she had been standing there as though turned to stone. Now she obeyed him, moving away on legs so tottery that twice she stumbled. Angelo was surprised by the depth of her fear. He assumed that the gun had been the cause.

Two years had gone by from the day he'd been given Lady Diana's last note, but he had never doubted for a moment how this affair must end. To Angelo it was all very simple. The Brothers had killed her as clearly as though they had put a gun to her head and pulled the trigger; and for this they too must die. He had appointed himself judge and jury, and tonight he would be hangman too.

He had held his hand until Darby had been laid to rest, because he had no wish to stir up a gang war for his old commander. Now it was simply a personal matter between the Brothers and Angelo, and he was very much aware of his own peril. Just one mistake, the minutest error of judgment, and he would never leave the Charmaine alive.

This was why he had instructed Massarda to wait twenty minutes, and not a minute longer. If he hadn't returned to the street within that time, it would mean that something had gone disastrously wrong. And if such ill chance should befall him, he wanted to be quite sure that his bride got safely away. The very thought of Sandra in the vengeful hands of the Brothers chilled his blood.

The first part of his plan worked like a charm. He had gone up the fire escape like a thief in the night, slipped through an unlatched window and down the corridor to the office without seeing a soul. And then to find all the four Cerdan Brothers together in the same room was, to Angelo, the answer to a prayer. It was only when he saw Arabella that he knew his luck had run out. There could be no witnesses to this night's work, and yet he was far too sentimental ever to harm a woman.

Sandra had been watching the minute hand move along with agonised eyes; and for once the smile had gone from the face of Massarda. He had kept the engine ticking over ready for an instant getaway; and with just thirty seconds left he was coming to the decision he dreaded above all others. If he kept his promise and drove off there could be a new life for Sandra; but almost certainly it would mean that there could be no life at all for Angelo.

However, as those last few seconds ticked away, the decision was virtually taken out of the hands of Massarda. A thunderous explosion rocked the Charmaine. The windows of the office on the first floor were blown out on to the street and flames began to rise from the roof. Without a second's delay, Massarda let in the clutch and the Bugatti began to move.

Max, having received Carlo's nod, had opened the safe and was stacking the notes upon the desk. Angelo moved forward and casually placed a small parcel beside them. And as he did so he saw the pictures of Arabella. He understood instantly. His gods had been kind to him after all. He gathered them up and motioned for Arabella to join him. "I think," he said to her, "we keep each other's secrets, you and I."

And without waiting for an answer he steered her towards the door, took the key from the lock and smiled grimly at the Brothers. "With the compliments of a lady," he said, "a lady named Diana."

The Brothers watched him go and heard the key turn in the lock and still couldn't comprehend; for the money lay untouched upon the table. Then a hissing snakelike sound came from the parcel and they understood at last. Angelo didn't want their money. He wanted their lives.

In terrible panic they began to shout; but this room rebuilt for their special pleasures had become their tomb. No one could hear them. They rushed to the window in a bid to toss the bomb out on to the street; but the shutters had been closed too securely for sudden withdrawal.

Outside in the corridor, Angelo had given Arabella an urgent push towards the stairs. "Go down quickly," he commanded, "mingle and know nothing."

Then he turned and ran the other way towards the back of the building. Virtually every guest in the Charmaine would be able to recognise his face. At all costs he had to stay out of sight. Still running, he went up the stairs, pushed open the hatch and climbed out on to the roof.

He was still on the tiles when the explosion rocked the building. A blast of hot air loosened his grip and he slithered feet first towards the edge of the roof. He was just about to wave the world goodbye when his fingers gained purchase at last ... on the guttering itself ... and by then he was suspended in space with the hard pavement far below.

He remained hanging at arm's length for a moment waiting for his senses to clear; and then using his wiry strength he swung himself hand over hand along the guttering and prayed that this rusty ironwork wouldn't crack beneath his weight.

He reached the drainpipe with an audible sign of relief and began to slide down the darkened side of the building. He had chosen this escape route, reasoning that the explosion would draw everyone to the front of the Charmaine.

As his feet touched the pavement the Bugatti coasted up beside him, the back door opened and the urgent hands of his bride pulled him inside. The wheels hadn't even stopped turning as Massarda slid the red roadster away through streets that were suddenly coming alive. They could already hear the fire bells and the sirens.

A full minute went by before Massarda spoke and by then the old familiar laughter was back in his voice. "You're a lucky man, my friend," he said. "I offered to take your bride away on her honeymoon, but she has strange tastes. She prefers you. She made me circle the block one last time."

He kept within the legal speed limits until they were clear of London. Then he smoothly built up that power until the needle was flickering at ninety; and a few seconds later, he let in the supercharger which had been specially fitted for this day's work. They were soon rocketing down the highway at just over one hundred and twenty miles an hour with Massarda's foot flat against the boards.

The near-perfect alibi was being created. No jury in the

world could ever be convinced that a man had boarded an ocean liner in Southampton one hour and a half after leaving his wedding reception, and still found the time to commit mayhem somewhere along the way. But that's what happened.

Massarda arrived barely a minute before the gangplank was due to be raised. There was just time for a swift, strangely shy kiss from Sandra and a hug from Angelo.

"As one married man to another," said Angelo, "give my love to Anne."

And then with a wave they were gone.

With the police patrolling the streets, George Mills had taken Sewell to the safest haven of all, the flat of Buck Emden's widow Claire.

As the door opened he announced, "This is Georgie Sewell. He's just done Alfie Solomons."

It was the magic password. The door opened wider and they were quickly ushered through to a quiet backroom. Claire Emden, a big, blonde raw boned woman, had heard the hubbub on the streets below and yet was totally unruffled by the notion of harbouring the fugitive.

"Did you do him in style?" she asked.

By way of answer, Sewell held up his mangled hands and she looked at them in some wonder. "I reckon that calls for a drink," she said, reaching for a bottle of wine. She had lost the habit of smiling since the death of Buck, but she was smiling now.

They stayed there drinking, saying very little, for a couple of hours until long after the hunt had died down. And she tended his hands with a gentleness that one wouldn't have expected to find in such a big, strong woman.

Finally he rose and straightened his tie in front of the mirror as he always did before stepping out on to the street.

"Where are you going now?" she asked.

He shrugged. "Home," he said soberly. "Without Darby, there's nowhere else to go."

For the Sabinis and for the Cobblestone Fighter, the

story that had begun on a hot summer's night in the Griffin had run its course.

Conclusion

Charles 'Darby' Sabini has been described to me variously as a prince of a fellow and a ruthless racketeer; and doubtless the truth lies somewhere in between.

Certainly he could be ruthless. He may have looked upon violence as a last resort, but when the need arose he didn't hesitate to send out his razor teams — the most feared war machine of the day — in pursuit of his enemies. When his own soldiers, even close friends such as Fred Gilbert and Silvio Massarda, incurred his displeasure they suffered the same fate and carried their scars to the grave.

Despite his quiet voice and easy-going ways, he was a dangerous man. The big black gun he carried was no theatrical toy: on at least two occasions it took him uncomfortably close to the brink of murder. Just suppose the gun had jumped in his hand when he shot Billy Kimber and the bullet had flown a little higher; just suppose the gun hadn't misfired so providentially on Epsom Downs …

There was kindness in him too, as he showed by coming to the aid of Louisa Doralli and Sandra Mancini, two girls who had been outlawed by the society in which they lived. And for the children of Little Italy, he proved to be the softest of soft touches. Many of them knew him as 'Uncle Bob' because every time he saw them he gave them a shilling. Men who couldn't pay their rent and were in danger of being cast out of their homes would go for help to Darby; and invariably he would reach into his pockets and hand over a fiver. He had never been known to ask for repayment: men usually repaid the fivers because they wanted to be able to ask again, but for no other reason.

There could be no doubting his courage. His lone stand against the mob in Brighton's Russell Hotel was the stuff of which legends are made. Horatius on the bridge above the Tiber couldn't have bettered this.

And despite his lack of schooling, there could be no doubting his intelligence. His foresight and planning were almost Machiavellian in their complexity. He had the ability to outwit his enemies over and over again. He repeatedly frustrated the forces of law and order with his ability to think ahead . . . for instance, anticipating that he would be searched for that big gun firstly in the courtroom during the Cortesis' trial and then at the Derby. And the shenanigans surrounding the Epsom ambush bore the mark of genius.

If a man is to be judged by the friends he makes along life's road, Darby would emerge with some credit. He was a man for all seasons; and his chosen companions were of all ages and of wide-ranging character.

A Scotland Yard commander known as Charlie Artful came to like and respect him. A gangland strongarm man known as the Cobblestone Fighter — a loner selective in his choice of friends — was the one who termed him a prince of fellows. Nino Zoff and Angelo Gardini, two young Turks with only a limited respect for their elders, chose to admire him above all others. And even that prima donna of an advocate, Sir Edward Marshall Hall, found him to be a character to savour.

But he was by no means a plaster saint. He was wily, cunning and totally streetwise. He had come to realise early in life that every man has a price. With that thought as his guiding star, he corrupted the police as they had never been corrupted before. Such bribery would often begin in the most innocent of ways. Off-duty policemen coming into the Griffin or the Yorkshire Grey would find a pint tankard on the bar, courtesy of Darby Sabini; and it would have seemed churlish to reject such a friendly gesture . . . particularly as it came from a man who had never been to prison. That was the first step down a slippery slope. Later, as Darby came to know them better, he would listen to their tales of woe, lending a sympathetic ear; and if they needed a little help with their son's school fees, a wife's birthday present or maybe just the rent, then like the good fellow he was, he'd be only too happy to help out.

Yet despite this, he had a very real respect for honest citizens and it was his proud boast that "no honest man has anything to fear from me." I once raised this with Georgie Sewell, pointing out that many of the bookmakers feared him greatly. The Cobblestone Fighter had a simple answer to that. "Darby didn't look upon bookmakers as honest men," he said.

There was some reason for that: in the twenties and thirties, the dividing line between the two camps often became blurred. Many bookmakers were gangsters; and many gangsters were bookmakers. Darby himself in his younger days had been a bookie's runner in the employ of fight promoter Dan Sullivan, while Alfie Solomons was just one of a host straddling the fence.

It was fashionable during the racecourse wars to look upon the bookmakers as the persecuted ones; but this wasn't always the case. Many bookies had their own bully boys who were there to make sure that their boss showed a profit at the end of the day. They would sometimes take the tickets of winning punters and then walk away . . . leaving some silver-tongued bookmaker to explain that, much as he might like to, he really couldn't pay out on the strength of the poor punter's word alone.

Then there was Darby's double-edged morality. Here was a man who would happily fill his gangland coffers with money extorted from bookmakers and club-owners on the ground that the Sabinis provided a fairer deal than the gangs who had gone before. It was seemingly all right to set out with his war wagons, raid the headquarters of other mobs, break heads and take their money. But it most definitely wasn't all right to use bad language in the presence of a woman, to embarass a lady in public or to pick a pocket on St Peter's Day; while for Darby, the pimps and the ponces would remain for ever beyond the pale.

He was a mysterious man who chose to blur the edges of his personality, so that no one ever completely understood him. He liked to keep even his closest companions slightly off-balance, because this gave him an edge over all men. The simple rig he'd chosen to wear was designed to make him look like the peasant which he most certainly was not. He had a gift for persuading others to underrate him, usually to their cost. This played a major part in the downfall of the Trimmer on that historic night in the Griffin and it also lured Billy Kimber down his own road to destruction.

As it was impossible to know what went on in the backrooms of Darby's mind, it was perhaps inevitable that myths should be fashioned around him.

One of the most popular of these has been the belief that Darby Sabini was in reality a Mafia chieftain with direct links to Sicily. This seems unlikely, to say the least, for he was at best a lukewarm Italian. His Italian father had died when Darby was only two-years-old and thereafter he was raised by his English mother. There is no record of him ever going to Italy. Most of his friends were English, and when the war came he regarded himself as a patriot, being immensely proud of his son's role as a fighter pilot in the RAF.

The other Saffron Hill legend is that when Darby retired to Brighton, he took with him two sacks filled with gold; and that these mysteriously disappeared, so that when he died, he died penniless. Yet his clerk Jimmy Napolini, when stopped while leaving the country, was found to have £30,000 in his possession.

It was an odd finale for Sabini, who had created the most lucrative criminal empire ever seen in Britain. Darby had been a tutor in the finer arts of gangsterdom and his influence lived on for a while.

Alf White set up the King's Cross Gang which dominated the racecourses for a while. Bert Marsh and Albert Dimes became the lieutenants of Billy Hill. And Angelo Gardini became the first member of a small army of Sabini soldiers who emigrated to Brooklyn and joined forces with the crime family of Joseph Profaci. They later linked up with Crazy Joe Gallo in what was to become the last of the Mafia wars seen in the city of New York.

So how, I wonder, will history remember Charles 'Darby' Sabini . . . as the protector of Little Italy, as a warlord, as a romantic singer of songs, as a ruthless racketeer, as a man of his time, or maybe as a mixture of all these?

Of just one thing you can be sure. We won't see his like again.

In the True Crime Library series: